Seeking Perfect Health

SPIRITUAL SECRETS TO STAYING HEALTHY

selected writings of
Sri Chinmoy

ISBN 978-0-9957531-2-9

Blue Beyond Books Limited
4 Paget Road, Ipswich
IP1 3RP, United Kingdom

www.bluebeyondbooks.co.uk

Printed in Serbia

Contents

Editorial Note

Sri Chinmoy's words presented here have been selected from his writings, lectures and answers to questions, which he offered to spiritual seekers, university students and luminaries from all walks of life over the years. In the process of compiling this book – which included occasional excerpting text from longer passages – we have strived to stay true to the original context and convey Sri Chinmoy's philosophy as he expressed it during his life. However, may we suggest to the interested reader to explore the original, unabbreviated versions of the texts, which can be found at www.srichinmoylibrary.com.

Preface

Health and wellbeing – we all value it. But health and wellbeing are not merely matters of things physical. You can eat and exercise perfectly, yet still struggle with your overall sense of wellness. Because we humans encounter life on multiple levels of consciousness – we experience things physically, emotionally, mentally, and deeper on spiritual levels – overall wellness is a matter of outer fitness and inner fitness.

Indeed, while we might fall ill from something purely physical – we might bruise ourselves falling or catch a cold from a damp draft – more often being unwell has its source in something deeper. We might have emotional or mental stress. We may be out of touch with our innermost nature.

In Sri Chinmoy, we find someone who is recognised as both a good and great spiritual teacher, and a leading advocate for wellness in the most complete sense of the word. Sri Chinmoy's teachings are those of a contemporary teacher who emphasises the relationship between the inner life and the outer life. With appropriate inner discipline, we create the foundation for a healthy and productive outer life. Again, maintaining a strong physical body is of paramount importance for sustaining a viable and fulfilling inner life.

In this insightful book, Sri Chinmoy addresses this integral relationship between the inner and the outer. From the inner perspective, we will learn how to utilise prayer, meditation and other inner disciplines for the purpose of improving health. We'll also learn the value of mental attitude towards illness. These are not merely philosophical abstract constructs. Sri Chinmoy offers concrete and valuable insights and techniques that can be used every day for the sake of our overall wellness.

Again, from the outer perspective, Sri Chinmoy addresses the role of physical fitness in improving the quality of our inner life. With guidance on how best to use exercise, diet and breathing techniques, Sri Chinmoy enables the reader to achieve a life that is both strong and fulfilling.

Perhaps most importantly, we learn about the concept of consciousness. Indeed, learning how we can better manage our consciousness, not only for the sake of health, but also for tackling all life's challenges, is integral to achieving a balanced and happy life.

The most valuable aspect of this illumining book lies in reminding us that every action we take reflects, and carries with it, the consciousness we embody while performing the action. The words themselves are endowed with the loving consciousness of a great spiritual teacher. In the end, we discover that reading this book is healing in itself.

– Dr. Pradhan Balter

1

A Fully Awakened Body

I try to be integral – physically, vitally, mentally, psychically and spiritually. I feel that we should do everything together. That is why I do so many different things. God gave us the body, vital, mind and heart. Each one is part of our existence. We try to bring the best out of them for manifestation. Whatever is good inside the body should be brought forward for its manifestation, whatever is good inside the mind and so on.

Down the sweep of centuries, there have been many spiritual Masters who did not believe in physical fitness. They felt that if you devoted time to taking exercise, then you were not meant for the spiritual life. Only by living in the Himalayan caves could you practise a spiritual life. If you accepted life, then you were not spiritual because you had descended. That was our ancient Indian theory.

Now we have made progress. We try to accept both God the Creator and God the creation. If we accept only God the Creator, if we do not see God inside others, then God created us in vain. Now we have accepted God the creation and we are trying together to bring down peace, light and bliss from Above.

Unfortunately, the physical does not respond to the spiritual so easily. We are involved in the outer world twenty-four hours a day, but our inner life is the real life that brings down the divinity from Above long before the outer life. First we try to bring down the divinity from Above or bring to the fore the divinity from within and then we offer it to the physical, to the outer world.

The physical and the spiritual are of equal importance. For us, the physical is the temple and the spiritual is the shrine. If there is no shrine inside a temple, people will laugh. What kind of temple is it? Again, if there is no temple, the shrine will not exist for long. So the temple and the shrine, the body and the soul, go together.

Some spiritual Masters say, "Who cares for the temple, as long as there is a shrine?" They neglect the body. But if you neglect the temple, what will happen to the shrine? The wind will come and blow it away.

Similarly, if we pay all attention to the body-temple and do not care for the soul-shrine, then we shall always have self-doubt. We will be convinced that we cannot do something. Now we can say, "I can do it, I can do it," because we know that God is inside us. If we have to depend on our physical body alone, then we will find that we cannot take even one step. But if we know that Somebody else, God, is doing it in and through us, then unlimited steps we can take.

Your body was not meant
To saunter down lethargy-lane.
Your body was meant
To challenge death to a constant duel.

Physical fitness

Physical fitness is of great importance in our life. If the body is in good condition, then we can perform all our life-activities well. So it is important to run or do physical exercises every day in order to become strong, healthy and dynamic. If we are physically fit, we will be able to keep ailments and other uninvited guests from entering into us.

In the past, people cared for the fitness of the body because they knew that if they had a healthy body, then they would be able to stay on earth longer. If they were spiritual people, they felt that a healthy body would enable them to continue praying and meditating for many more years. Today also we know that if the body is full of sickness, then we will not be able to pray and meditate well. For weeks and months we may suffer both physically and spiritually.

We have the body and we have the soul. A spiritual person has to give equal importance to both the body and the soul. If he pays attention only to the body, if he becomes physically strong but spiritually very weak, then for him there will be no peace of mind or inner happiness. Again, if he pays attention only to prayer and meditation and neglects the body, then his body will not be a fit instrument to reveal and manifest God. In the morning he will try to pray to God, but he will have to stop because he has a headache, upset stomach and so forth.

If someone does not get any exercise at all, then the physical will remain unlit, lethargic and a real hindrance to the aspirant. If the physical consciousness does not aspire, it will remain separated from the soul. Then rest assured, you will never be able to achieve perfection. The physical has to aspire in its own way to increase its capacity so that it can hold light. Then the physical will contribute to the spiritual and you will be able to aspire and manifest much more. So physical fitness and spirituality must go together. It is like having two legs. With one leg I cannot walk; I need two legs to reach my destination.

The more progress I can make physically, vitally, mentally and psychically, the more love, the more joy and the more goodwill I am able to offer.

Question: I understand that you place great importance on taking care of the physical body. Would you please tell me why you do this?

Sri Chinmoy: You come from Japan. In Japan, let us say, there is a Shinto temple with a beautiful shrine. If you value the shrine and everything else that is inside the temple, you will make sure that the temple is kept in good repair so that it will not be blown away if there is a storm. If the temple is not in good condition, then the shrine cannot last. Similarly, inside the body is the heart and soul. The shrine is within. We have to make the body a fit instrument to house the shrine; we have to keep the grounds of the temple in good condition if we care for what is inside the temple.

I am trying to become good, better, best – not in order to defeat you, but in order to love you better. The more progress I can make physically, vitally, mentally and psychically, the more love, the more joy and the more goodwill I am able to offer you. If I become a better person, then I can give you my good qualities. But if I remain a bad person, then I will have nothing to give you. If my body is not in good condition, if I have a headache and an upset stomach, then early in the morning I will not be able to get up to pray and meditate. If I do not pay attention to the physical body and keeping the body fit, my spiritual life will suffer and

I will not be able to offer you my goodwill, love and joy in my prayer and meditation. That is why physical health is of great importance.

Question: What is the importance of physical fitness?

Sri Chinmoy: With our soul's aspiration and our inner dedication and surrender, we will be able to reach the Supreme Truth. After we realise the Supreme, we have to fulfil the Supreme by manifesting Him on earth. But in order to manifest the Supreme, the Highest, on earth, physical fitness is absolutely necessary. If we want to reveal and manifest Him, the body must be our divine instrument. If the physical is not fit, manifestation cannot take place at all, or it can take place only to a very limited extent. For that reason we have to pay some attention to sports and exercise. Otherwise, we shall be weak and sick all the time. That does not mean that we must be the world's fastest runners or best athletes. But we must keep the body fit, according to the necessity of our inner development.

The body needs proper training so that it will be fit to receive the message of the soul. If the body is strong and healthy, it can receive the message of the soul unreservedly, and we can become a perfect receptacle, a perfect instrument. At that time the soul's aspiration and the body's aspiration go together.

So please exercise regularly. Your strong body will someday be necessary for the manifestation of the Supreme. The higher, the deeper you go, the more it will be necessary for you to reveal and manifest your inner divinity; and for that manifestation, physical fitness is of paramount importance.

Physical, subtle and causal bodies

Question: For what purpose do we have a physical body?

Sri Chinmoy: The soul, which is a conscious, divine portion of God, has to live inside the physical body in order to make progress. Inside the church is the altar. Similarly, the body is a temple, and inside the temple is the shrine, the soul. The body is our outer protection and, at the same time, our instrument for physical manifestation. Without the body the soul is helpless. Until manifestation takes place in the physical world, we cannot offer the real Truth to the world at large. The purpose of the body is to manifest the Reality of the soul. The soul needs the body to manifest the inner Truth, the divine Truth; the body needs the soul to realise the highest Truth. When the soul inspires us to do something, it also gives us the necessary capacity. Unfortunately, the unaspiring body, vital and mind do not obey the dictates of the soul. The body, vital and mind give us messages, but these messages are not the inner dictates of the soul. The desires of the body often directly contradict the divine necessities of the soul, because this material body is unconsciousness itself.

When a person begins to aspire consciously, his entire being gradually starts to aspire. His soul aspires, his heart aspires, his mind aspires, his vital aspires and finally his body aspires. When the physical in the aspirant starts to become one with the soul's inspiration and aspiration, then God's Light can find a fit receptacle in him.

Question: What is the difference in physical appearance between the physical body and the subtle physical?

Sri Chinmoy: The body is a solid, tangible form. But inside the body, with the same form as the physical body but without physical substance, is the subtle body.

Question: Is it possible to see the causal or subtle body?

Sri Chinmoy: The causal body can be seen only by realised souls and great spiritual aspirants. Ordinary persons cannot see the causal body. And most ordinary persons do not see the subtle body either. The subtle body is often seen and felt when our kundalini is awakened, because the kundalini is in the subtle body. It is also seen and felt when a new light descends into our physical body. When a new light descends, in that light all of a sudden we can see the subtle body. There are also other ways to see the subtle body.

When we see the subtle body, we get true confidence in our existence. Right now we contradict ourselves at each moment. This moment we say that we are something and we have something; the next moment we say that we are nothing and we have nothing. But if we frequently see our subtle body, then we get the true confidence that we possess something that is worth having and worth showing.

> *The capacity of the body is limited –*
> *Yours, mine, everybody's.*
> *But the capacity of the soul is unlimited –*
> *Yours, mine, everybody's.*

Question: Do you mean that the subtle body is a less dense form of matter? Does it interpenetrate or live within the physical body?

Sri Chinmoy: The subtle body is undoubtedly less dense than the physical body is. We really have three bodies. As we go deep within, these bodies become more subtle. Each person has what is called in Sanskrit *sthula sharira*, the physical body. Inside the physical there is another body, called *sukshma sharira*, the subtle body. Inside the subtle body is a third body, called *karana sharira*, the causal body.

Before the creation started – the creation that we see all around – *Hiranyagarbha* existed. *Hiranyagarbha* is a Sanskrit word that means golden womb (*Hiranya* means gold and *garbha* means womb). Our physical eyes will never be able to see or feel this *Hiranyagarbha*, but it is there that the seed of creation originally germinated. From there the causal body came into existence.

The purpose of the body is to manifest the reality of the soul. The soul needs the body to manifest the inner truth, the divine truth; the body needs the soul to realise the highest truth.

In the causal body we have all qualities in seed form. In the subtle body we begin to get the manifestation of some things that are in the causal body. Finally, we get truth, reality, experiences and realisation in the gross physical body. The physical body is like a huge banyan tree, which grows from a tiny seed. When we compare the physical body with the causal body, it is simply unbelievable. This is how the manifestation takes place: from the causal to the subtle, and from the subtle to the gross physical.

The causal body has the capacity to fulfil us, but it fulfils in the process of time, through the evolving wheel, which we call evolution. With the causal body the journey begins, but it is with the physical body that we fulfil ourselves, and the universe fulfils itself, through the outer form.

By physical, we mean the outer consciousness of the universe. In its seed form this is *karana sharira*, but eventually this seed grows into the boundless universe. When it expands, it automatically reaches the highest. You may say that expansion and reaching the highest are two different things. But in God's case, in the soul's case, it is not like that. What touches the farthest corner of the universe is meaningless if it has not also reached the highest. God will never remain unfulfilled, and He will never allow us to remain unfulfilled either, so we are bound to reach the highest, farthest and deepest.

Question: Do the causal and subtle bodies last longer than the physical, or are they all impermanent?

Sri Chinmoy: The causal body, the subtle body and the physical body are all, to some extent, impermanent. They lose their existence when the soul leaves the body. As soon as the soul leaves, the physical dissolves into the five elements. But sometimes the causal body stays for a longer time with the soul than the physical and subtle, because the soul's potentiality is within it in seed form.

Then, when the soul reincarnates, it takes a new causal, a new subtle and a new physical body. First it takes a causal body. Then from the causal comes the subtle body. The subtle body is like the outer body, but we do not see it until we have the inner vision. Then comes the outer body.

Question: Is it true that all diseases begin in the subtle body and then manifest in the physical body?

Sri Chinmoy: It is not necessarily so. This is one theory, and it has a kind of truth. But many times the imperfection starts in the physical body itself with no prior connecting link in the subtle body. The gross physical body is not aspiring, and there is some imperfection in it: so it gets diseases.

When a disease attacks the subtle body before coming to the physical, and the person is aware of it, then he has time to fight and prevent it from entering the physical body. But if it attacks the physical directly, then the victim has almost no time to prevent its entrance.

Question: Can the subtle body appear in other places?

Sri Chinmoy: The subtle body, which looks and acts exactly like the physical body and can be perceived by others, can appear at one place while the physical body is at another. We leave the physical behind, and with the soul's light we give form to the subtle physical at any place we want. The things that the soul can accomplish in a fraction of a second will take twenty years if we have to do them in an ordinary earthly way.

But while the soul and the subtle physical are outside the gross physical, the body must not be touched or disturbed in any way. If it is, it loses its purity and divinity, and decay begins immediately. Then the soul finds it very difficult to return. Even under excellent conditions, the soul must return to the body before 11 or 13 hours, or it will find the door closed.

Question: Which of these three bodies gets psychic experiences?

Sri Chinmoy: All of them. Once one gets a real spiritual experience, one sees that experience in all three bodies. When it is a matter of realisation, one sees, feels and becomes the Truth in all three bodies. This is not the case for minor experiences. If it is just an ordinary earthly happening, which is not so important, only the physical or the subtle body will get it. But if it is something serious, important and significant, then the experience will be recorded in all three bodies.

Question: How do you develop consciousness in your subtle body?

Sri Chinmoy: Consciousness is already in the subtle body. Consciousness is functioning most powerfully, vehemently and soulfully in the subtle body, but it is not functioning here on the physical plane. So you should try to develop consciousness in the physical body, the ignorant, lethargic physical body.

Consciousness descends into the subtle body from the causal body. Consciousness means God in His infinite forms with infinite capacity. In the subtle body everyone has enormous capacity. It is in the physical that we do not have capacity. These three bodies are like three rungs of a ladder. The third rung, the physical, is not receiving what the second rung has to offer. The infinite potentiality from the causal body descends into the subtle. But because the physical is not aspiring, the subtle is not strong enough to give this capacity to the physical. The subtle is more than ready, but if the physical is not aspiring and trying to ascend, if the physical is not making some conscious effort, then there is no meeting place.

How can you feed and develop the physical consciousness? You can develop the consciousness in the physical only through proper self-discipline. Two things comprise your daily life: doing something or not doing something. If something wrong presents itself, don't do it. If you see something right, do it. In that way your consciousness automatically expands. When you do something wrong, you bind your consciousness. If you are caught by temptation, which you cannot overcome right now, try to delay your action for a little while. Delay it until tomorrow. Then, when tomorrow comes, delay it until the day after tomorrow. In this way keep on putting off the wrong action. In the meantime you will be doing many good things, and on the strength of these deeds you will be increasing the number of soldiers in your divine army. Then it will be easy for you to overcome temptation. In this way, the consciousness in the physical can be developed.

Question: Do the nerves of the subtle body have any correlation with the nerves of the physical body?

Sri Chinmoy: No. If you cut a physical nerve, the subtle nerve will not be affected at all. But you can bring messages from the subtle nerves into the physical; you can bring energy and other wealth from the subtle into the physical. The purpose of the subtle nerves is to give energy to the subtle physical. By your concentration you can strengthen your subtle nerves.

Question: They say that there are tens of thousands of subtle nerves. Are they distinct enough to actually be counted?

Sri Chinmoy: Yes, the nerves are quite visible to the inner eye. They are not at all entwined; they are very distinct. But they are very light and delicate, very subtle. Once I tried to count them. I think that I counted two or three thousand and then I did not want to count any more. I said, "I believe it."

Question: How can we strengthen our subtle nerves?

Sri Chinmoy: Sometimes our subtle nerves are weak, so we have to strengthen them. When you meditate, for a few minutes, say four or five minutes, consciously breathe in and out, inhale and exhale, very, very quietly. This is one way we can strengthen our subtle nerves. There are other ways, but this is the easiest way, the most effective way: to sit properly and breathe in and out as quietly as possible. This will help the subtle nerves become strong.

When a disease attacks the subtle body before coming to the physical, and the person is aware of it, then he has time to fight and prevent it from entering the physical body.

Question: Is it possible for the physical form to live in two worlds at once?

Sri Chinmoy: You need not have two physical bodies to live simultaneously in two worlds. One physical body is enough. If you have greatly developed your spiritual faculties, you can function not only in two worlds, but in many worlds or in many places at the same time. The physical body will be in one place, but you can get the knowledge of some other place, some distant place either in this world or in some other world, from your intuitive faculty, your inner vision or your inner beings.

The transformation of the body

Question: How can one divinise the human body?

Sri Chinmoy: There are two methods to divinise and transform the body. One is through constant aspiration, for the physical to aspire along with the soul. The other is through evolution. After going back to the soul's region and returning to earth many times, the soul will gradually reach a stage at which it will be able to act here on earth the way the Supreme wants. At that time, it will be in a position to transform the body from within.

Question: Does your philosophy say that the body always has to be an obstacle in the communication with God and can never be a part of our self-offering to God?

Sri Chinmoy: No, the body need not always be an obstacle, a hindrance to God-realisation. The body is unconscious right now, true. But it need not always be so. An infant is unconscious, but that does not mean that he will not grow into childhood, adolescence and adulthood. Let us regard the body as an unconscious child. The child will grow through the inner nourishment it gets from the soul on the strength of our aspiration. When a child goes to school, he gets knowledge. He also gains inner wisdom day by day. Similarly, when we pray, concentrate and meditate, we are invoking Light inside us, and this Light tries to permeate our whole outer existence.

You are absolutely right when you say that the body is a hindrance. It is a hindrance for a long time, until the Light of the soul comes forward and takes charge of the body. But if you say that the body will constantly and eternally stand against the soul, then you are making a mistake. If the body were to stand permanently against the soul's possibilities, then nobody would be able to realise God. For God-realisation takes place only on this planet, only on earth.

In the beginning it is absolutely true that the body stands against the soul's progress. But there comes a time when the soul comes to the fore and compels the body to become its faithful, perfect instrument. This achievement represents the victory of both the body and the soul. When the soul consciously makes the body feel what it should do, and when the body is willing to listen to the dictates of the soul, then the body and the soul run together. At that time, realisation, revelation and manifestation become inevitable. When we are advanced, when we are nearing our Goal, we see that the physical consciousness is totally merged in the psychic consciousness, and we see the body in its transformed luminosity. The soul and the body become part and parcel of the one Truth, and that Truth is God the infinite.

There is a piano and there is a pianist. Both are equally needed to produce music. If there is no instrument, how can the player play? And again, if there is no player, the piano cannot function. Similarly, the soul needs the body in order to fulfil its highest mission. And the body needs the soul to give purpose to its existence, to realise the Highest.

> *My soul's only sacred dream:*
> *My body will be totally transformed.*
> *My body's only secret dream:*
> *My body will breathlessly listen*
> *To the dictates of my soul.*

2

Seeking Perfect Health

The source of the healing force is God, the all-Good. God is omnipotent; again, He is all Love. So it is from His Love that the healing power comes into existence.

Health and the law of karma

Question: If one is in generally good health, what would cause pain and aches in the body?

Sri Chinmoy: It is one thing to have good health and another thing to deliberately maintain good health. Unless you are consciously keeping good health, at any moment you may be attacked by some forces. It is like having a large amount of money without knowing about it. If you are not conscious of it, you may easily lose it. If you are not conscious that you have a flower, you are likely to lose it. Anything that you have must have some place in your awareness. You may have good physical health, but perhaps in two months' time you have not thought of your body once, let alone tried to increase the strength of your legs or arms or to get some extra capacity.

Unless you touch something every day, it does not shine. Often I have told people to touch the furniture in their homes every day.

As soon as you touch something, it gets new life. If you are aware of something, immediately it shines and gets a new luminosity. If you have good health, if you touch your health every day, it gets new life. By giving attention to something, you give new life to it.

Why do we experience suffering? In this world we are always consciously or unconsciously making mistakes. When we consciously make mistakes, we are quite aware of it. But unfortunately, we do not see the millions of things that we are doing wrong unconsciously. These unconscious mistakes manifest themselves in the physical world and the results come to us as suffering. In the case of ordinary unaspiring human beings, after tremendous suffering, sincerity dawns and the soul leads them to knowledge and wisdom. If people who repeatedly make mistakes have sincere aspiration and want to know why they are suffering, then the soul's light comes to the fore and tells them. If we are spiritual people, consciously we will not do anything wrong, but unconsciously we do many things wrong. We can prevent unconscious mistakes only through our aspiration, prayer and meditation. If we aspire, then God's Grace and Compassion protect us.

Question: How much of illness is due to karma and how much is due to physical factors?

Sri Chinmoy: It is a very complicated matter. Sometimes the constitution of an individual is not strong, either because of hereditary factors or from lack of nourishment during childhood. So he is a victim to sickness quite often. Or sometimes the wrong forces get pleasure by attacking an aspiring soul. They know that they cannot destroy the individual, but they can delay indefinitely his progress, achievements and success. If in the morning we get a headache or stomach pain, how are we going to have our best meditation? If we are physically sick, how can we meditate?

So when we see that we are being attacked, we have to be extra alert. If we are not conscious or careful all the time, then we open ourselves to the wrong forces. In some cases, the wrong forces attack us because we cherish them. Early in the morning I have exposed myself to cold. I know I will catch a cold. I know I will suffer in a few minutes, but I am enjoying the cold. You can call it lethargy or making friends with hostile forces. So here, when hostile forces attack us, we get a kind of perverted joy and it becomes a kind of hopeless case.

But even if we are cautious, still the wrong forces can attack. We have bolted the door, but even then the hostile forces try to enter and steal things from us. But if we leave the door and windows open, they will have more opportunity to attack us. If we are careful and cautious, then there is less opportunity for the wrong forces to attack.

Thoughts and physical illness

Very often physical illness will start in the mind. If you can stop it there, then it will not attack the physical. Now, how do you know if it has entered the mind? Easily you will know. Take the mind as a room in your house. If somebody has entered your room, naturally you will know. Before illness touches the physical, at least five or six times you will get some inkling in your mind. You are driving your car or talking or resting and all of a sudden you feel some uneasiness. It is not something serious at that time. It comes in a thought-form that is not wholesome or progressive. One thought that is not progressive can easily bring disease into the mind, into the vital, into the physical. If the thought is stagnant, like a stagnant pool, then problems arise; from there disease starts. Any thought that is not progressive is dangerous.

A seeker can easily trace a negative thought before it touches the physical. Take the mind as the third floor in your house. If there is water leaking up there, easily you can stop it before it flows down to the second and first floors. If you do the needful on the third floor, then you don't have to suffer on the other floors. When you notice something wrong in the mind, the best thing is to immediately invoke the Light and Peace of the Supreme. If you have Light and Peace, illumination and peace of mind, then the wrong force will be illumined. Either it will be frightened to death and leave you or it will be transformed by the Light and Peace that have entered the mind.

So all the time, while you are thinking or talking to friends, you have to know whether the thoughts you are using, or allowing to stay in your mind, are progressive or not. If you see a thought moving forward, then you should keep it. But if it is moving instead just like an insect, then it has to be thrown out. We have to be very careful of our thoughts, because we live in a mental world, a thought-world. One thought can take us to Heaven or to hell. Each thought is either nectar-like or poisonous. Each thought can be our saviour or it can be our destroyer.

Question: Is there any way that we can avoid minor illnesses like colds?

Sri Chinmoy: Certainly. We can avoid them if we can pay attention to their first warning in the mental plane. In the mental plane we get a warning, but we neglect it. We feel that it will not come to the physical plane. As soon as we notice that we are going to get an attack on the physical plane, we have to fight against it. Just to notice the warning on the mental plane is not enough. We have to fight against it immediately. Otherwise, from the mental plane it will come to the vital and then to the physical plane. While it is in the mental plane we do not pay attention to it; therefore, it starts descending. Once it comes to the vital plane it becomes very difficult to stop it. And when it reaches the physical it is most difficult.

No disease, not even a little cold, can immediately attack us on the physical plane. First it attacks on the mental plane. But we do not know what is happening on the mental plane because most of the time we remain in the physical consciousness. So until the ailment has attacked our physical body we are not aware of it.

You will not have to go to the doctor at all if you become more conscious of these things. Since you are all seekers, every day you pray and meditate. All these things come to you during your prayer and meditation. But sometimes you feel that you are so powerful that the illness will not attack you. Or you feel that even if it comes to the physical, still you can easily conquer it. Another problem is that the human body is so undivine that it cherishes disease. Why? So that people will sympathise with it. When somebody says, "I am so sorry you are sick," immediately we feel that we have achieved something.

Exercise

Chanting For Physical Strength

If you are physically weak, if your physical constitution is not satisfactory, you can chant sincerely and soulfully:

> *Tejohasi tejomayi dhehi*
> *Viryamasi viryam mayi dhehi*
> *Valam masi valam mayi dhehi*

If you chant sincerely and soulfully, in a week's time you will see a change for the better in your health. This chant means:

> *I pray for dynamic energy;*
> *I pray for dynamic virility;*
> *I pray for indomitable physical strength.*

Sickness and spiritual development

Question: What is the best way to make inner progress through pain and sickness? I am sick so often.

Sri Chinmoy: The best results you will get when you feel that you are not the one suffering. Feel that Somebody who loves you so much is suffering in and through you. That is the best way for you to make the fastest progress. God loves you so much. He loves you infinitely more than you love yourself, but He wants to have an experience in and through you, which you are calling pain. You are suffering, suffering, suffering. You have to feel that Somebody loves you so much, and He feels that this is the best way for you to make progress.

You are not invoking or inviting the pain, the suffering and all the ailments that you so often get. You are not inviting them and you are not enjoying them. Some people enjoy getting an ailment so that they do not have to go to work. When they have a headache or a stomach upset, they intensify it. If they have a headache, they make it into a migraine headache. By putting force into a silly headache, they can justify to themselves that they do not have to go to work. First they magnify their pain and then they justify why they do not have to do this or that.

When you are suffering, you should not say, "God does not want me to work for Him. That is why He is giving me this pain. God wants somebody else to make the fastest progress. God has given me this pain so that I cannot make progress." The human mind will think this way, but the heart will say, "God loves my physical body infinitely more than I can ever love my body, but He Himself is having an experience in and through me which I do not understand and I do not have to understand." Then you can make the fastest progress.

Question: When the physical body is not in good condition, how can we still make the fastest spiritual progress?

Sri Chinmoy: I am the right person to answer your question! My physical body is suffering so much. There are many people who suffer physically but who make faster than the fastest progress. And again, there are many who are physically fit but who do not think of God, do not think of inner progress.

Many elderly men and women, unfortunately, are not physically fit. It is true that if you are physically fit, then you get joy, you get freshness, you get more inspiration to aspire. But if, for certain

35

reasons, you are not physically fit, what can you do? At that time, there is only one way you can solve the problem. You have to offer gratitude to God because you are still cheerful, you are still happy, you have not revolted against God.

You think you are so unlucky because you cannot easily walk. But you do not know what kind of problems are in the minds of the other people who are moving around so easily. Millions of problems they have. Your only problem is that you are unable to walk as fast as they do. Are you not lucky? Your only problem is that your pain is not allowing you to walk as fast as others do. But this is on the physical plane. On the mental plane, you have no idea how much other people may be suffering.

People who do not have the capacity sometimes are lucky because they can make surrender – let us not call it helpless surrender, because that is very bad, but cheerful surrender. You can say, "O God, You did not give me the capacity to do something, to perform something, but my gratitude-prayer to You is that whatever You have given me, I should be satisfied with."

Very often physical illness will start in the mind. If you can stop it there, then it will not attack the physical.

So if you are satisfied with what you have, then you can make the fastest progress. There is another way you can be satisfied with what you have: just look around. You will see that there are many people who are suffering much more than you are. If you go to the hospital, you will see how many are in infinitely worse condition than you are. When you think of your suffering, think of the hospital. Then this thought will be your immediate medicine. That is what I do. Sometimes, when I can walk only with utmost difficulty, I think of some human beings who cannot walk, cannot move at all, and my suffering seems like nothing in comparison to theirs. At that time, I say to God, "O God, You are so kind to me. Still I can walk a little, whereas so many people in Your creation cannot walk at all."

Again, why should I have to make comparison with other people in order to make myself happy? That is only a temporary solution. The first way is by far the best way. You have to say to yourself, "I will remain happy. Who can be suffering more than God Himself inside me?"

We feel that God is all Happiness. But God is everything. God is not only inside our suffering, God is suffering itself. Let me just give an example. When a little two-year-old child has got some serious ailment and is suffering, the identification of the mother is such that she suffers far more than her little child. How much a mother can suffer! A mother's identification with her child goes to the very root of the child's suffering.

So here, also, if we take God as our Mother or Father, we have to feel that He is suffering much more than we are. We feel that we are the sufferers. But if we love God, we will feel that inside us Someone is not only suffering as much as we are, but He is suffering much more because He has the capacity to absorb, to receive, to feel everything more than we do. In that way, the Supreme suffers more than we can ever suffer.

Again, there is a purpose in our suffering. We do not know why. So our attitude should be only cheerful surrender to God's Will. You will definitely pray to God for better health – that is the right attitude. But, while praying to God for better health, you have to offer gratitude to God because you are still happy and you have not revolted against Him.

Question: If one has ill health, is spiritual perfection attainable?

Sri Chinmoy: Ill health is a complicated term. Somebody's physical constitution may not be as strong as it should be, but that is not ill health. When we use the term ill health, that means there is some ailment in the physical. Now, even if there is some ailment in the physical, spiritual light can still easily enter into the physical. If you are not physically strong, it does not mean that the highest Light or highest spiritual Height cannot enter into you. No, it can and it does. There have been many spiritual Masters who had a weak physical constitution or who did not have sound health. Just because you cannot sit properly or cannot walk properly does not mean that real perfection, divine perfection cannot enter into you. No! Real perfection, inner perfection, is not affected by any kind of ailment or physical shortcomings.

But if it is some serious internal disease like cancer, or tuberculosis, or leukaemia, then the physical has to be totally cured if the seeker is to achieve total perfection. If it is not possible for the physical to be cured within a specific period by earthly means or medical aid, the body should at least try to be receptive so that the Divine Light from above can enter it and slowly and steadily cure the physical ailment. In this way, the body will become fit to hold boundless Light.

Question: How does physical pain, illness or an unpleasant experience affect meditation?

Sri Chinmoy: Suppose you have a headache or stomach upset. Then how will you meditate? In real meditation, the entire being has to aspire. But in my case, I have occult power. So even if I have a 40 degree or 41 degree fever, when I want to meditate I can go up to my highest height.

Your meditation is also affected when you are angry with someone and you have not illumined your anger. You may have forgotten your anger, but if you have not illumined it, then it will pull you down. You have many unpleasant experiences during the day. A few hours elapse and then you forget the experience. "Forgotten" is the right word, but "forgiven," no. Unless you have forgiven, you have not illumined the anger. Anger is not now coming, but still it has pulled you down seven rungs of your consciousness-ladder even though you have totally forgotten the incident. Sometimes you will quarrel with the members of your family and then you will go to sleep. But the next morning you cannot meditate. You have totally forgotten the incident, but while you were sleeping the strength of the anger increased. The velocity, the speed, the strength of the anger from seven hours ago will be greater. It is just like a swarm of insects that are multiplying like anything. But positive forces increase slowly. So when something has gone wrong, it is better to rectify it and illumine it immediately.

Everything on the physical plane has to be illumined before you meditate. Otherwise, meditation cannot be profound. If one part of your being is not properly balanced, you cannot have good meditation. Even breathing can affect meditation. Here you are not sick, but because something is wrong with your breathing system, you cannot have a good meditation.

There are some unbalanced persons who feel that they will realise God by walking along the street like a vagabond or by torturing their bodies and remaining weak. Their physical weakness they take as a harbinger of God-realisation. The great Lord Buddha tried the path of self-mortification, but he came to the conclusion that the middle path without extremes is the best. We have to be normal; we have to be sound in our day-to-day life. Aspiration is not one thing and our physical body something else. Our heart's aspiration and our physical body go together; the physical aspiration and the psychic aspiration can and must run together.

Overcoming pain
and physical suffering

Question: I would like to know if there is a way to transcend pain.

Sri Chinmoy: As long as we are in the physical, if our consciousness is all the time in the physical, certainly there is pain. But if we can withdraw our consciousness from the physical, then there can be no pain. Many spiritual figures have done it. They are undergoing a major operation, even without anaesthetic. Then what do they do? They put their conscious force on that particular place and then they smile. They smile while the operation is going on.

I remember one such incident. A girl cousin of mine went with one of her friends to the doctor. My cousin was undergoing an operation, a tremendous one. When the doctor started operating, she looked at the doctor and started smiling, but her friend, who was supposed to help her if she was crying, fell down on the floor and fainted. The actual person who was undergoing the operation started smiling! And I have seen quite a few times that the doctors in India do not use chloroform or ether.

Once I had three big boils and the pain was unbearable when I went to the doctor. I raised my hand; the nurse was holding my wrist and I was looking at the doctor, smiling. Before the actual operation took place, for ten minutes I was concentrating. When the doctor was operating, I was looking at him, smiling.

There is another way to overcome pain. If you can consciously enter into the pain itself and stay in the pain for a few minutes, then the pain does not torture you as pain. For when we become the possessors of the pain, we can transform this very pain into joy. When you enter into

40

the pain, you become the possessor of the pain. Right now, the pain possesses you; you are a victim of the pain and it keeps torturing you. But if you can possess the pain, you can actually inject into that area anything that you want. With your conscious power, you can inject delight, joy, whatever you want. It is quite possible and practicable. Many people have done it and the doctors have admired it. If you want to inject joy into the pain, you can feel it in that very spot.

Then, of course, if we can separate ourselves from the body-consciousness, it becomes easy. Ramana Maharshi suffered from a cancerous tumour. He used to laugh and say, "That gentleman has now come." "That gentleman" referred to the pain and he mocked it. Pain can easily be transformed into joy if we consciously enter into the pain or if we separate our body-consciousness from the pain itself. In two possible ways it can be done. Either you can enter into it and possess it and when it is possessed, you can give it your own joy. Or you can separate your body-consciousness from the pain itself. These are two possible ways.

Even if there is some ailment in the physical, spiritual light can still easily enter into the physical.

Exercise

Overcoming Pain

You should try to invoke Light in order to cure pain. Pain is, after all, a kind of darkness within us. When the inner Light or the Light from Above starts functioning in the pain itself, then the pain is removed or transformed into joy. Really advanced seekers can actually feel joy in the pain itself. But for that, one has to be very highly advanced. In your case, during your prayer or meditation you should try to bring down Light from Above and feel that the pain is a darkness within you. If you bring down Light, then the pain will either be illumined and transformed or removed from your system.

Question: Does God feel physical pain?

Sri Chinmoy: Definitely. Although He is above and beyond the physical, He feels physical pain, for He has become one with the physical. He is in the physical, He is in the subtle, He is everywhere. If He lives in the physical, then naturally He feels pain. People thought that the plant did not have any feelings. Now scientists have discovered feelings in the plant and they can even show how the plants quarrel and fight as we do. So naturally God is there. When we attack someone on the physical plane, we suffer; and because He is within our suffering, God suffers. But at the same time, He is beyond our suffering. For us it is not like that. Each time we get a blow, we stay in the suffering. But in God's case, he is inside the house and He can come out of the house at any time. He knows how to open the door. But we are like children: we don't know how to open the door and we don't know how to close the door. God is like the elderly person who escapes with His wisdom. If He does not want to use His wisdom, he can stay and play with us and He can be bound. The moment He enters into us and enjoys our game, He enters into our ignorance, although He has the capacity to come out at any moment.

God feels physical pain as you do. To be very frank, God feels pain much more than we do because He identifies with our physical, vital, mental, our entire being. This is God in His human aspect. In this personal aspect He suffers from our pain. He enjoys everything that we do in our own way. He is in our life of pleasure. He is in our life of limitation and imperfection. The personal God suffers and becomes everything in life.

But God in His impersonal aspect does not feel anything. He is not at all attached to our suffering. He only transforms and liberates us with the conscious awareness and assistance of the personal. Without the assistance of the personal God, humans would not make any satisfactory progress on earth.

We have to consciously cooperate with the divine dispensation, with the human God. God takes the help of certain human beings so that He can transform the human into the divine. As long as He remains in human beings and identifies Himself with the human, He does feel pain as you do, infinitely more than you do.

Question: If God is all-loving, why does He permit suffering?

Sri Chinmoy: 'Suffering' is a term we see in the dictionary. When we suffer, we feel tremendous pain inside us; there is no joy inside us. But I wish to say that suffering is a state of consciousness. When we practise spirituality and yoga, we feel that this suffering is nothing but an experience. And when we dive deep within, we feel it is not we who are having this experience of suffering; it is God Himself. He is the Creator; He is the creation. He is the Doer; He is the action itself. So the more we identify ourselves with the Source, the more we feel that what we call suffering is not suffering at all. It is an experience that God Himself is having in and through us for the fulfilment of His infinite Vision. I call it suffering, you call it suffering, but God does not call it suffering. He calls it an experience. It is a state of His own infinite Consciousness.

Question: Nonetheless, the person who is suffering, in the common sense of the word, is in pain.

Sri Chinmoy: He is in pain because he has identified with the earth-reality. But if he identifies with God, then the suffering itself will be turned into delight.

Question: If I drop a hammer on your foot, will you feel suffering or will you feel delight?

Sri Chinmoy: If I remain in an ordinary consciousness, then I will feel it as suffering. But if I am in a divine consciousness, then either I will take it as delight or I will take it as an experience of God in and through me.

If we can withdraw our consciousness from the physical, then there can be no pain.

At the age of eight or nine I had a serious operation. I told the doctor I would like to watch the operation. The doctor said it was a serious operation, but I said, "No!" Right before the operation I put a very concentrated force on it, and during the operation itself I was smiling at the doctor. The doctor was horrified. On the strength of our concentrative power, we can transform suffering into delight itself if it is God's Will. And again, if we want to experience the suffering and take it as an experience, we can do this. But if we do not transform suffering into delight, and if we do not take it as an experience of God in and through us, then it will hurt us deeply.

Healing injuries

Question: How can we spiritually heal injuries?

Sri Chinmoy: It is a matter of inner capacity. One kind of capacity is to heal the injury by bringing down peace and light from above. Another kind of capacity is to ignore the pain altogether. During your meditation, if all of a sudden you have intense aspiration, then you can bring down more light from above to cure your injury. But you have to do this consciously during your meditation. If during the day you casually say, "Oh, how I wish I didn't have any pain!" that will be useless. But while you are meditating, if you suddenly remember your pain, that is the time to pray and bring down more light.

Again, you can increase your capacity to tolerate pain. Now you have pain, let us say, but still you run; whereas if you had had the same kind of pain four years ago perhaps you would not have been able to run. Again, sometimes the pain is unbearable and it is absolutely impossible to run. Then what can you do? But if it is bearable, try to run according to your own capacity. At that time, don't think of how fast this person or that person is running. Just go according to your own capacity and remain cheerful. All the time think that you are running only against yourself.

Again, if it is beyond your capacity to ignore the pain, in addition to praying and meditating, you can also go to the outer doctor. Light is also inside the doctor. But in some cases there is no way to cure the pain.

Question: Why do we get injuries for no apparent reason?

Sri Chinmoy: There is always a reason, either in the inner world or in the outer world. In the inner world, if something is dislocated – if your consciousness has descended or if some hostile forces have attacked – you get an injury. Sometimes you are totally innocent, but the wrong forces, the malicious forces which are hovering around, can cause injury.

Again, sometimes in the inner world or in the thought-world you have done something wrong, and this can also cause an injury. Thought can be more destructive than a hydrogen bomb. Wrong thoughts, which are so destructive, may come and attack you, especially your physical, which is in ignorance most of the time. The wrong forces find it very easy to attack the plane, which is fast asleep, because they will encounter no opposition there.

So, in the inner world either your consciousness has descended because of wrong thoughts, or some hostile force has attacked you, and that is why you get an injury, which you cannot see any reason for.

Question: If you have a sports injury – for example, a calf injury – is there any way to inwardly heal it totally?

Sri Chinmoy: Everything has to depend on prayer and meditation. Again, outer therapy is also of supreme need. Then, if you can take minor stretching exercises to strengthen the calf, it may help. But if the exercises create more pain for you, then I advise you to go to a therapist. Of course, the most important thing is the inner prayer. But it is like a boxer using two hands. With one hand you cannot do everything. God created medical science. You should take as much help from medical science as possible, and at the same time you have to think of our spiritual science, which is prayer and meditation. They have to go side by side. First, of course, since we are spiritual people, we have to give preference to the aspiration-aspect of life, and at the same time we have to give considerable importance to medical science. God is also operating in and through medical science.

Question: Always when I become very interested in the physical and playing sports, I injure myself to the point where I have to stop completely. Why does this happen?

Sri Chinmoy: What actually happens in your case is that when you enter into the physical world – playing tennis or other things – you do not give value to the physical as such. You remain in the mind. A portion of your existence you throw into the game and another portion you keep totally in the mind-world. It is like cutting yourself in half. You are keeping your body on the first floor, but your consciousness is always on the upper floor, in the mind. If you can direct more of your mental energy into the physical when you play, this will not happen.

You want to play; you want to win. But actually the concentration of the mind, the real concentration, is not in the physical itself. You know that you are playing tennis, but the concentration that the body needs from the mind is not there. There is a gap. The body without concentration from the mind is helpless. So, when you play, do not think of your mental work. Your mind may not be aware that it is thinking of the wrong thing, but it is one thing not to be aware of doing the wrong thing and another thing to concentrate consciously on the right thing. Inside you and all around you there are many beings. Because there is a gap between the mind's concentration and the physical activity, these beings can attack the physical. They need not actually be wrong forces, but they may create unfortunate experiences in life.

Suffering is a state of consciousness. When we practise spirituality and yoga, we feel that this suffering is nothing but an experience.

Question: They say in bodybuilding, "No pain, no gain." To me, that sounds ridiculous. I've never been in pain. Bodybuilding is the fountain of youth – you get stronger as you go along. I've made gains without pain. Why do people feel they have to hurt themselves to improve themselves?

Sri Chinmoy: I see eye to eye with you. Not only bodybuilders but also many other athletes are of the opinion, "No pain, no gain." But I wish to say that if God is standing at a particular place and I am supposed to reach Him, will it please Him more if I hurt myself and then run towards Him on one leg, or will it please Him more if I use both legs and run in a normal way? Either I can use my wisdom-light or my stupidity-height. If we say that only by hurting ourselves can we improve ourselves, it is almost like saying that we should overeat in order to strengthen

Take as much help from medical science as possible, and at the same time you have to think of spiritual science, which is prayer and meditation.

ourselves, that we should eat voraciously so that overnight we can become stronger than the strongest. That is not possible! Slowly and steadily we shall try to increase our capacities, not by leaps and bounds, which can cause us injuries.

I find it difficult to accept the theory that physical pain is unavoidable in order to improve. True, we may at times get pain as we struggle with an exercise or with heavy weights. But that is a totally different matter. If we deliberately torture our body beyond its limited capacity with the hope of becoming stronger overnight, then there is every possibility that the body will revolt. This kind of training will tell upon our health.

Everything has a capacity of its own. This capacity has to be increased intelligently, and, in the case of a seeker, also soulfully. A seeker knows that he does not have to disable or damage any part of his body to prove to God how much he loves Him. He does not have to say, "Here is my love for You: I have come to You with my arms and legs impaired." It is ridiculous. God wants us to come to Him as soon as possible. Injuring our bodies will in no way increase our speed. I am speaking here about spiritual progress, but even from an ordinary point of view, wisdom will not tell us to inflict pain upon ourselves just in the hope of gaining something valuable. Wisdom can show us the way to our destination without the intervention of pain.

Healing from a spiritual point of view

Question: What do you think of healing in relation to spirituality?

Sri Chinmoy: I wish to say a few words from the spiritual point of view about what I think of healing. Healing deserves special attention and, at the same time, special appreciation from spirituality. An ordinary healer heals a person in order to get name or fame or just because he has an inner urge to help humanity. But a spiritual person heals a particular person only when God asks him to or when he gets personal permission from God to do so.

When an ordinary healer heals a person, he is often affected by the disease or the ailment of the patient. Very often I come across people who have healed and then themselves become victims of those ailments that they have cured in some other people. Some actually die of the disease they have cured in others. But when a spiritual person cures someone, he cures with his soul's light. He enters into the sufferer with his soul's light, and he cures the person without becoming attached. There is a continuous cosmic flow in and through his life, and that continuous flow of cosmic energy enters into the patient from him. Then it is just as though light were permeating the entire body of the person who is suffering. So a spiritual person heals only when he is commanded by the Divine or when he gets special permission from the Divine. Then he becomes totally one with the sufferer on the strength of his soul's oneness, and cures with his soul's light.

Question: Does meditation include healing?

Sri Chinmoy: Meditation includes everything. In meditation we enlarge our consciousness until it includes everything in the universe. There is nothing we cannot achieve through meditation. Each individual has the capacity to heal if a person knows how to concentrate and meditate, and especially how to concentrate on physical ailments. There is no ailment in God's creation that he won't be able to cure. But we have to know if it is God's Will for us to heal someone. Otherwise, we may act like the hostile forces who want to break the rules of the divine Game.

There is a difference between healing that is done by an ordinary healer and healing done by a realised soul. The ordinary healer has learned some techniques for removing an illness from someone, but after some time he himself may become the victim of the diseases he heals in others. Why? Because he doesn't know where to throw the diseases after he has taken them away. If we take healing as a profession, if we just pray and think good thoughts for a few minutes and then go and cure someone, then we might be acting against the divine Force, the divine Law. It is in our deepest meditation that we come to know what we should do and what we should not do. If the Supreme asks us to heal someone, at that time He gives us the power, and when He gives

us the power, we are not responsible. The result immediately belongs to Him. But if we are responsible, we may be caught by the result of our own action. This is the difference between acting with the help of our meditation and acting out of our own so-called human compassion.

A realised soul only heals when God asks him to do so. He knows that in the cosmic Play of his Father, the Supreme, everything that happens is a necessary experience. He only intervenes when the Supreme asks him to. And when he heals someone's illness, he knows that he can throw the illness into the ocean, into his infinite Father who has commanded him to take it. He has no responsibility because he is an instrument of the Supreme. The ordinary healer thinks he is being supremely compassionate in healing others of their diseases, but is this healer more compassionate than God? God knows what experiences people need. If He wants to cure them of their illnesses, He will give the right instrument of His the power to do it successfully.

Question: Do you think it is possible for a seeker to cure physical illness through prayer?

Sri Chinmoy: Absolutely! Absolutely! Suppose your father is sick and you pray to God. If your prayer is soulful, then God will definitely cure your father if that is His Will. But even if your prayer is most soulful, if God wants your father to go through an experience of sickness, He knows what is best for your father as well as for you. Then you have to know that God Himself is suffering in and through your father. It is God Himself who is having that particular experience. But even if God does not cure your father, your soulful prayers will not be lost. God will fulfil your prayers in a different way. Since your prayer has knocked at God's Door, God will keep the sincerity, the soulful quality of your prayer inside His Heart. Your prayer God preserves as a peerless treasure. Then He will enlarge and expand your heart and illumine your life. He will give you a very big heart.

Today you are crying and praying for the cure of your father; tomorrow you will cry for ten persons; the day after for the vast humanity. At that time, you will pray not just for your near and dear ones; you will pray for all of suffering humanity. God will give you the divine capacity to pray for all of humanity.

> Good health
> Is the most significant gift
> From God.

Question: Could you say something about healing and spiritual development?

Sri Chinmoy: I do not encourage people to come to me just to get their diseases cured. If they become my disciples and meditate sincerely, then if it is the Will of the Supreme, naturally I will bring down light from above to cure them. There are many ways to help people, but the most effective way is to bring them closer to God. For that they have to consciously practise the spiritual life.

There are philanthropists who are helping people, giving alms to the needy and so forth, but they are not trying to illumine their own lives or others' lives. Unless one consciously knows what God wants from one's life, one is bound to make mistakes. Pride and ego will come forward. The first thing is to know what the Inner Pilot wants from one's life. Then one can help humanity.

Unless we can become one with our Source, it is impossible for us to help humanity the way God wants us to help and serve. But when spirituality is practised consciously, when one consciously cries for total, inseparable oneness with God, at that time God gives the aspirant boundless Light. Then the aspirant offers this light and slowly and gradually those who are actually meant to receive light from him will get it. But one has to be very careful to feel the real divine light

before one starts helping others. Otherwise, it will be like the blind leading the blind.

Question: If God is the Source and is capable of healing whomever He wishes, why do certain people feel that they have to go through a number of incantations, wave the hand over the disturbed area four times to the right, three times to the left and so on? Why these systems?

Sri Chinmoy: It is a matter of faith. Some people feel that if they do particular things, then someone will be cured, while others feel it is not necessary. You are dealing with individual faith. Some people use incantations in order to reach a higher state of consciousness, while others feel it is all within them, so it is necessary only to pray and meditate. You pray to God to give you the capacity to please Him in His own Way, and God will do the rest.

If I pray to God for His own fulfilment in and through my life, naturally He will do what is best for me. Some people pray to God, "God, grant me this. If I have this, then only will I be able to become a good instrument of Yours. I am now suffering from a headache and stomach upset. If You cure me, I will be able to have a good meditation." But others say, "No, I wish to please You in Your own Way. If it is Your Will that today I do not meditate, if You have something else for me to do, if You want to give me an experience of suffering, then this is best for me. I do not know what is best for me. What is best for me only You know."

Medicine
May cure my body,
But God alone
Can feed my heart.

Healing with prayer and meditation

Health loves to live
In the heart of hope.

Question: I find it very difficult to pray for anything other than health because health is so important. I feel selfish when I pray for anything else.

Sri Chinmoy: You are doing absolutely the right thing. When you pray for health, you are praying not only for the physical body but also for the mind, vital, heart and everything. If your health is not good, if you are suffering from a headache or stomach upset or some other ailment, then how will you be happy? Your mind will be occupied only with pain; your heart will be breaking. The best thing is to pray first and foremost for health. Afterwards, you can pray for other things that you would like to have.

Question: If a member of one's immediate family is sick, what is your feeling about praying to God for healing power?

Sri Chinmoy: Let us say that your mother is sick. Instead of saying, "Cure my mother, cure my mother," if you can say, "I place my mother at the Feet of God," you will be doing the best thing. Your best healing power will be to place your mother at the Feet of God, because He knows what is best.

When you offer your own will to the Will of God, you gain power, and this power will be utilised for God. God Himself will tell you how to utilise it. But if you try to heal on your own, in spite of your best intentions, you may stand against the Will of God.

Suppose you pray and meditate to acquire divine power so that you can cure people and help the world. You say, "I want to be a camel and carry the whole burden of the world on my shoulders." But if the camel is not illumined, then how can it help others gain illumination?

You are running towards your goal. If you ask God to give you something, then this is just an additional thing that you have to carry, and it may slow you down. So if illumination is your goal, think only of your goal and nothing else.

Again, if a remedy for a disease comes spontaneously from within and you don't have to exercise your mental power or will-power, then there is no question of ego, pride or vanity. If in your meditation, all of a sudden you see inner light, and in this light you get a cure for some fatal disease, then naturally you will be able to offer this inner illumination to the world at large. But otherwise, the best thing is to become illumined first. Then only will you be serving God in His own Way. Otherwise at times you will serve God in His own Way and at other times you will be feeding your own ego.

The medicine-doctor and the God-Doctor

Question: What is the best way to unite prayer and meditation with the study and use of homeopathic medicine?

Sri Chinmoy: Homeopathic medicine is more subtle than ordinary medicine. The subtler the reality, the stronger its capacity. Pure spirituality is subtler than the subtlest, and its power is beyond measure.

Homeopathic medicine should try to become one with the inner medicine, which is oneness with the Will of the Supreme. When the homeopath gives medicine to a patient, he should first pray and meditate. Then he should feel that he is offering the result of his prayer and meditation in the form of homeopathic medicine. He has prayed and has meditated, and he has got some spiritual essence and substance from his prayer and meditation. Then, on the human level he is giving this in the form of homeopathic medicine.

Some of the Indian homeopaths have done this and have been successful to a great extent. A friend of mine was of that type. He used to pray and meditate and then the reality that he received from his meditation he used to give in the form of homeopathic medicine.

Question: I work in a hospital and sometimes there are people who are terminally ill. What is the best way of dealing with those people?

Sri Chinmoy: Just try to be more compassionate and more loving. What you are doing now is absolutely right; only try to do it more. Feel that you are not doing anything wrong. You are doing the right thing. You may be criticised, but when you are doing something right and people misunderstand you, then what can you do?

There are two ways to serve mankind, the inner and the outer way. There are two ways of serving patients. One way is to talk to them and mix with them very compassionately. The other way is to offer good will, love and concern inwardly. If you feel that the inner way is not effective, then you are making a mistake.

There are two ways to serve mankind, the inner and the outer way. If you feel that the inner way is not effective, then you are making a mistake.

Question: I'm a doctor. Shouldn't I serve God in my patients first?

Sri Chinmoy: You are a doctor, true. But early in the morning, before you even see a patient, you have to think of God and meditate on God. Only then are you doing the right thing. Right now, you are seeing God in your patients. That is your heart's magnanimity. That is wonderful. You are seeing God in your patients, so you will be more careful, more soulful, in your dealings with your patients. That is what God wants. But this very soulfulness, this sympathy, this love and concern for your patients – where are you getting it from? You are getting it from your own heart, from your soul. But if you do not meditate, do you think you will continue to get it? If you do not observe silence or feel peace for a few moments in the morning, you will not get it. There are many doctors who are very undivine, callous, because they do not do the first thing first.

Early in the morning you are praying and meditating to God for a few minutes; that means that you have love for God. Then, when you go to the hospital, you are showing your love and devotion to the Supreme in others. So you are really doing two things and both are of considerable value. You are doing the first thing first; but you feel that only the second thing that you are doing is the right thing. No, both are equally right. You go from one step to the second step. You cannot take two steps at the same time. First you step on one leg and then on the other leg. So, in your case, you are doing absolutely the right thing. Early in the morning you are praying to God; that is your love for God. Then, the same love you are spreading to your patients, who are your brothers and sisters.

Question: Can you explain to us why a person who is very ill may continue to live on for days and days, even when this phenomenon is unexplainable in medical terms?

Sri Chinmoy: Medical science does not have the last word on life and death. The doctor may say that somebody's life will last only a few more seconds, but we see that days run into weeks, weeks run into months and still the person goes on struggling. Even though the soul withdraws and has no concern either for the world or the person who is suffering, the physical still wants to cling to the earth. It feels that if it can stay for even one minute more, then it will achieve something important. But this is not true. When the soul loses its concern, when it shows no interest in what is happening in the outer life, a human being can never have any higher or deeper experiences. But the soul is most compassionate: It allows the blind body to stay on earth for a few days or for a few months more. Even though the soul knows that the body's prolonged stay on earth is not serving any purpose in expediting the person's realisation, where the person has abundant attachment for this outer cloak, out of compassion the soul may stay in the human body for a short while just to please the unconscious human frame.

We all want to conquer death, but the soul knows what is best for us. The soul knows that if, at a ripe old age, one tries to linger and revitalise his life-energy, it will not help the individual. The soul has practically ended its journey for this incarnation. As regards the soul's growth, we can rest assured that the soul will not get any benefit, for it has already gathered the quintessence of its life-experiences.

Question: Is it always best for doctors to keep people alive as long as possible, or does it depend on the individual case?

Sri Chinmoy: If a person is spiritual, the doctors and relatives should always try to keep him on earth as long as possible, because spiritual people are always fighting against death. If somebody has the capacity to utter God's name soulfully just once more during his life, then he will achieve something in the soul's world. That achievement will be added to the other achievements of this life and in his next incarnation his life will be a little bit better.

In India some people live for over two hundred years, but they do not have time to pray to God even once in six months or a year. From a spiritual point of view, these people are like a solid piece of stone. For them each additional year is just another waste of time. But if one can stay on earth even one hour more and invoke the presence of the Supreme during that hour, then naturally it is better for that person to stay on earth. Even unconsciously if someone is thinking of God, then it is better for him to stay as long as possible on earth. That is why doctors should not give drugs that will make the patient unconscious, or put animals to sleep.

We have to know if the individual is aspiring or not. If he is a seeker, every second on earth is of paramount importance in God's Eye. If a person feels that just to stay on earth is enough for him, God may say, "All right. If that is your goal, you stay." But if somebody has a higher goal, if he has a real goal, God will give him the opportunity in every possible way to stay on earth and reach his goal. Otherwise, he has to come back again. Human life is like a constant battle. If you have been fighting for a long time and if you become too tired to continue, naturally you will go and take rest, and then enter into the battlefield again later. But if you do not become tired and if you do not have to go and take rest, then you will continue to fight against ignorance, against imperfection, for a long, long time, and perhaps you will win the battle once and for all. And once you conquer the undivine forces which are constantly attacking you, once you are successful, at that time you manifest God, the inner Divinity within you.

A true hospital
Gladly welcomes the suffering world.
A true doctor
Immediately heals the suffering world.
A true nurse
Inseparably becomes one with
The suffering world.

Excerpts from university talks on health and medicine

Pavlov State Medical University of Saint Petersburg
Saint Petersburg, Russia, 25 May 2004

Medicine

Before the lecture, Professor N.A. Yaitskiy, Rector of Saint Petersburg Pavlov State Medical University, presented Sri Chinmoy with a Commemorative medal on the occasion of the University's 100th anniversary.

Sri Chinmoy dedicated his talk to Raisa Maximovna Gorbachev.

I lovingly, soulfully and gratefully dedicate today's talk to the most glorious soul of my highly esteemed sister Raisa Maximovna.

There are four doctors: the medicine-doctor, the prayer-doctor, the faith-doctor and the God-Doctor. The medicine-doctor depends on earth-discoveries. The prayer-doctor depends on God-Compassion. The faith-doctor and the faith-patient work together to establish the satisfactory result for the patient. The God-Doctor decides what is best for the patient and does the needful in and through the medicine-doctor, the prayer-doctor and the faith-doctor.

God gets tremendous joy when these three doctors work together. Alas, it happens so rarely. The medicine-doctor prides itself on its stupendous capacity. The prayer-doctor gives full credit when its prayers are fulfilled to the ultimate Doctor, God. The faith-doctor gives credit to the medicine-doctor, more so to the prayer-doctor and infinitely more to the God-Doctor.

Medicine-doctors are physically visible and available. Alas, the innocent patient-victims pitifully suffer when the medicine-doctors enjoy their utter disagreements. The patient's life-breath plies between the compassion-medicine-doctor and the indifference-medicine-doctor.

With your kind permission, I wish to narrate a personal experience of mine. My right knee and I have been suffering from severe pain for the last twenty years. Not once, not twice, but thrice I have had sad experiences from my MRI examinations.

The doctors have differences of opinions. The first doctor said it is cartilage damage. The second doctor said that it is water inside the knee, unwanted water. The third doctor gave his opinion that it is rheumatism. My California doctors and New York doctors were in perfect disagreement.

Anyway, because of these three differing opinions I had to take treatment for all these three so-called ailments. To my greatest sorrow, my right knee still suffers unbearably, unimaginably.

There is an Irish saying: "God made time; man made haste." There are some doctors who are compassion incarnate. They give all their time, energy and concern to cure their patients, while there are other doctors who have no time, no time. Time is fleeing away and their concern is also fleeing away faster than the fastest.

It is true that no matter how much concern, how much love one has as a doctor for his patient, only if it is the Will of God does the patient continue to live on Mother Earth. But the kindness, concern and sympathy of the doctor for the patient give tremendous hope and joy to the patient. This hope and joy are not wasted.

We believe in reincarnation. When the patient goes to the other world, he or she carries with them their inner existence. And when the soul comes into the world with a human body once again, this particular patient of the past, brings down the concern, hope and all the good things that the patient received in his previous incarnations from the medical science. No good deed can ever end in vain. Today's good deeds are bound to be fulfilled at God's choice Hour.

I have mentioned the unfortunate negligence and indifference of certain doctors, but again there are many doctors, to my deepest joy, who are aspiration, concentration and dedication incarnate. Their concern for the recovery of the patient can only be felt and never be described.

Spirituality and medicine are two great doctors. Spirituality dives deep within to cure the malady. Medicine explores here, there and all-where to cure the malady. If the divers and the explorers work together against ignorance, the root of all diseases, then it will be remarkably easier to conquer each ailment.

The body suffers from countless diseases. It starts with a headache and ends in cancer. The mind suffers from many diseases. It starts with anger and ends in self-doubt. The heart suffers from many diseases. It starts with depression and ends in insecurity. Life suffers from many diseases. It starts with ignorance and ends in self-destruction.

Physical diseases are difficult to cure. Mental diseases are more difficult to cure. Psychic diseases are still more difficult to cure. Life-diseases, alas, are almost incurable.

Medical science is not the supreme authority on life and death. Spirituality, because of its conscious and inseparable oneness with the Will of the Absolute Supreme, has and is the supreme authority on life and death.

At times, medical science proudly predicts that the patient will die sooner than at once. But, to the greatest happiness of the patient, the patient gets a compassion-life-extension for three or four decades from Above. Spirituality does not and cannot perform this miracle, but spirituality unmistakably knows how the miracle was performed and Who was behind it.

About thirty years ago, I was fortunate enough to offer a soulful talk on medical science to a medical university in Cebu City in the Philippines. Just because it was a medical university, there were quite a few doctors and nurses who were kind enough to be present.

Prayer comes from the inner world and medicine comes from the outer world. Both are equally important. The inner world and the outer world must work together.

I said to the doctors that if some individuals are in a tug-of-war, and if two are on one side and on the other side there is only one individual, there is every likelihood that the side that has two will win. Similarly, if the man of prayers and the man of medicine are on one side in the tug-of-war and against them there is only one player, ignorance, then naturally the side that has two members is going to win.

We must work together. Prayer comes from the inner world and medicine comes from the outer world. Both are equally important. The inner world and the outer world must work together. Then it will be quite easy for us to conquer the world that stands against us. We must not work independently. We must work interdependently.

If spirituality and medical science play their roles interdependently, like inhaling and exhaling, then God's Heart-Garden will be inundated with earth-beauty and Heaven-Fragrance.

I shall deeply appreciate it if the audience would kindly join me in singing a short song that I have composed for this occasion. As I said, we must work together, together. With our prayers, with our songs, in all our activities, if we work together then we are bound to be successful in our lives.

> *O four doctors, four:*
> *Medicine-Doctor, Prayer-Doctor,*
> *Faith-Doctor, God-Doctor!*
> *I bow to you four!*
> *You give me health-preservation-lore.*
> *You show me health-perfection-shore.*

In all sincerity, I wish to say that this particular University has given me boundless joy and boundless satisfaction. I bow to the medicine-world. I bow to the medicine-world. I bow to the medicine-world. I pray to God for your continued success and progress to elevate the sufferings of humanity.

National Health Institute
St. Petersburg, Russia, 27 May 2004

Health

The Scientific Board of the National Health Institute conferred the degree of Honorary Doctor of the National Health Institute upon Sri Chinmoy "for his outstanding contribution to the maintenance and strengthening of the health of the peoples of the world." The Diploma of Honorary Doctor was presented to Sri Chinmoy by the Rector of the National Health Institute, Professor P.P. Gorbenko.

The National Health Institute: this very name is so inspiring, aspiring, illumining and fulfilling. Health is of paramount importance and the nation pays all attention to health. I am extremely happy and deeply honoured to be here to offer my dedicated service to this great Institute.

Man's health
Is
God's Wealth.

Man's health-perfection
Is
God's Heart-Satisfaction.

The body is the temple.
The soul is the shrine.

The body is the dreamer.
The soul is the fulfiller.

No health,
No journey forward,
    Upward
    And inward.

Health-infirmity
    Is
Death-proximity.

The body fears;
Death nears.

National Health Institute,
To your vision-light
I bow and bow.

National health-smile is
Nation's victory-adventure
    Guaranteed.

Health-perfection
    Defies
Disease-intervention.

Stark poverty
Is not the only cause
Of ill health.

Health-attention-discipline-bankruptcy
Is the main cause
Of poor health.

Health-imperfection
Is the order of the day.

Therefore, military-disease-army
Ruthlessly attacks and damages
        The body-fort.

Man's body-perfection
        Is God's
Dream-Harvest-Satisfaction.

Man's body-perfection
        Is God's
New creation-inspiration,
New creation-aspiration
And new creation-manifestation.

I pray to God,
Not for the body of a boxer,
Not for the body of a wrestler,
But for the body of a God–believer,
God-lover and God-server.

I pray to God to bless me
With perfect body-fitness,
So that I will not be cowed down
By the buffets of disease-dragons.

I pray to God to bless me
With a Divinity-Illumination-surcharged body,
So that I can manifest here on earth
God-Infinity's Peace
And God-Immortality's Bliss.

Not body-comfort-indulgence,
But body-competence-effulgence,
Humanity's singular need.

There is an Indian saying from the hoary past:

Nayamatma balahinena labhya.

The soul cannot be won
By the weakling.
The soul can be won only
By the brave.

I wish to offer my prayerful and soulful gratitude to the authorities of the National Health Institute for having given me the golden opportunity to be of service to the soul, the heart and the life of this Institute.

I shall pray for the stupendous success and enormous progress of this great Health Institute, for the outer success and inner progress of this inspiring, aspiring and self-giving Health Institute.

The body's health is essential. Inside the body is the soul, our inner existence. What we need is physical fitness, not physical supremacy to defeat others and glorify ourselves. We need health, physical fitness, which is of paramount importance. When we are physically fit, we can achieve the things that we need most in our life. It is only through physical fitness that we can achieve what we desire and fulfil our lofty aspiration. Therefore, we must keep our body always fit to love God and to serve God in humanity.

Russian Pediatric Clinical Hospital
Moscow, Russia, 1 June 2004

Oneness-Heart

The Scientific Board of the Research Institute of Pediatric Hematology conferred upon Sri Chinmoy the title of Honorary Professor "for his outstanding contribution to the development of pediatric hematology and oncology in the Russian Federation". The Diploma of Honorary Professor was presented to Sri Chinmoy by the Director of the Research Institute, Professor A.G. Rumyantsev before Sri Chinmoy delivered his lecture at the Russian Pediatric Clinical Hospital.

There are three worlds. The first is the world of love, concern, sympathy and the feeling of oneness. In the second world, we quarrel, we fight, we strangle and we destroy our enemies. The third world is the world of suffering, suffering and suffering – unimaginable suffering. Most of us, if not all, live at different times in these three worlds.

This Research Institute represents the suffering world. Here we know, we see and we feel what the suffering world is. But again, we can bring into this world the world of love, the world of prayers. The doctors who are all compassion and affection, like these three[1], can do so much for the improvement of the suffering world, and they do it most devotedly.

This Institute deals with blood. People give blood, which is of paramount importance, on the physical plane. Again, we can offer blood on the inner plane also. We can offer blood through our prayers. The

---

1   Director of the Research Institute of Pediatric Hematology, Professor A.G. Rumyantsev, Head Doctor of the Russian Pediatric Clinical Hospital, Professor N.N. Vaganov, and Deputy Director of the Research Institute of Pediatric Hematology, Professor E.B. Vladimirskaya, who have been cooperating with "Oneness-Heart Tears and Smiles" Humanitarian Service offered by Sri Chinmoy Centres worldwide.

outer world and the inner world always go together. As we sow, so we reap, for ourselves and for others. Physically there are many, many who are unable to offer their blood to the needy; but spiritually, by virtue of their prayers, they can offer their inner blood to these sick children. Our prayers can be of tremendous help to these helpless children.

I am a man of prayers. I started praying consciously, sincerely and seriously at the age of seven. Then I started doing other spiritual disciplines: concentration, meditation, contemplation and so forth. But I still pray and pray. I pray for the improvement and betterment of the world. Like me, there are many people who pray to God for the betterment of this world. I am not the only one – far from it! There are countless people who pray to God most sincerely.

Sometimes God does not listen to our prayers. That does not mean our prayers are not sincere. Our prayers are sincere, but God knows what is good for us and what is good for the suffering patients. He knows what is really best for the patients. The human in us suffers hopelessly when our dear ones are snatched away by death. But if we pray and meditate, we clearly see that God has a special purpose when He takes away our dear ones from this world. After all, nobody can be as dear to the patients as God.

We live in the physical world. There is another world which is right now invisible to us. Again, by virtue of our prayers and meditations, we can establish an access to that particular world. Here on earth we work. After some time we become tired and then we take rest. We have a living room and we have a bedroom. We work very hard in the living room. Then we need to take rest in the bedroom before we can again enter into our outer activities. In exactly the same way, after we end our journey here on earth, we go to another place, which we call Heaven. There we take rest.

Here on earth when we lose our dear ones, we are heartbroken. In this world there are a few things that give us comfort or reassurance so that we can live on earth. With money-power we sustain our earthly life. We cannot put money-power inside a coffin; we cannot take it with us to Heaven or send it to our dear ones there. But our prayers, our goodwill, our concern, our self-giving breath: these currencies our dear ones can carry to the other world. There, these currencies are valued. The souls receive our love, our concern, our feeling of oneness. When the souls leave this world, they carry our goodwill, our love, our compassion, our concern and our self-giving will to Heaven. There they can use it. Our self-giving, in a sense, is a currency, and this currency they carry with them to use in Heaven. Our self-giving is of tremendous, tremendous need and tremendous help at the same time.

Sympathy, sympathy, sympathy: sympathy is our oneness-power. Sympathy can inundate us with the feeling of oneness. This Research Institute, which is all sympathy, has the capacity to bring to the fore our most precious quality: the feeling of oneness.

God is the Patient and God is the Doctor. It is God the Doctor who is trying to cure the God the Patient, or God the Doctor who wants the God the Patient to go to the other world, the higher world. Unfortunately there are human doctors who may not be aware of God's constant Presence. They may not feel that God Himself is acting in and through them. But if they have a sympathetic heart – which these three doctors right beside me have in boundless measure – then God becomes extremely, extremely proud of His medical children.

I have come here, not to speak; I have come here only to sympathise. I have come here to offer the tears of my heart. The little drops, the little tears that I have, I am offering to this vast ocean of tears. Again, when my tears, your tears and everybody else's tears are put together, our tears, which are founded only upon sympathy, become sweeter than the sweetest. Our oneness-heart-tears become sweeter than the sweetest. These tears do not break our hearts; these tears unify us. Our hearts sing God's Victory and pray for God's Victory to be manifested in and through each human being on earth. Our oneness-heart-tears are sweeter than the sweetest, and these tears make God truly proud of us.

My doctor-brothers and doctor-sister, I am offering you my love, my appreciation, my admiration and my adoration for what you are doing to cure the suffering world. In silence we pray. Our prayer is our service. Again, our devoted service is our prayer. We try to cure the patients with our medical discoveries and medical capacities. We try to cure the suffering world. To your noble and self-giving hearts, my oneness-heart I am offering, along with my gratitude and gratitude from the inmost recesses of my heart. My prayers shall be always with you. I have been praying for you in all sincerity since I first came to learn about this Institute.

This Institute is an Institute of sympathy, an Institute of oneness. When there is oneness, we feel that fulness looms large. We are full, we are complete, on the strength of our sweeter than the sweetest oneness.

Let us eat and drink
According to the need of the body.
Let us love and give
According to the need of the soul.
Let us reveal and fulfil
According to the Need of God.

3

Healthy Nutrition, Diet and Cooking

Conscious cooking

*O*uter fire we need to cook.
Inner fire we need to liberate.
God's Fire we need to love.

Question: What is the most important aspect of cooking?

Sri Chinmoy: The most important aspect of cooking is its life-energising reality.

Question: What are some ways to maintain purity in cooking?

Sri Chinmoy: There are many ways. But the main way, the most important way, is to repeat the name of the Supreme or to repeat the name of the cosmic goddess Annapurna. If one repeats her name while cooking, then one is bound to be inundated with purity.

Question: Is it significant whether food is raw or cooked?

Sri Chinmoy: It entirely depends on the taste of the individual. Raw food has a more energising quality than cooked food, but for the sake of taste we cook many foods. We can't deny it; cooked food is more tasty than raw food.

Question: Is there a special consciousness in which to cook for adults, children or other age groups?

Sri Chinmoy: While you are cooking for children, if you can maintain an innocent feeling along with your purity, then it will be of great help to the food-consciousness. While cooking for adults, if you can maintain a very dynamic quality, then it will be of great help to the food-consciousness for adults. And while cooking for the aged, you can try to maintain a very soft and tender feeling. You can try also to have a feeling that you are helping the old people to gain a new life. But especially a tender feeling and a concerned feeling will be of tremendous help if you cook for the aged.

> *The body's food*
> *Is matter-made.*
> *The soul's food*
> *Is spirit-made.*
> *Gratitude-life,*
> *Gratitude-heart for God*
> *Is food for the soul.*
> *Perfection-cry*
> *Is food for the soul.*
> *Heart's awakening*
> *Is food for the soul.*

Question: How does the cleanliness of the surroundings affect the food you cook?

Sri Chinmoy: The cleanliness of the surroundings does not immediately or directly affect the food. First it affects the consciousness of the cook. When the cook is affected, then naturally his product will be affected.

Cleanliness is of paramount importance, purity is of paramount importance and good feelings towards the pots and pans are of paramount importance. Everything is of paramount importance from the beginning to the end when you cook. Again, while cooking it is always advisable to speak as little as possible so that you can remain in your own highest consciousness. Otherwise, your consciousness may remain high, but the person with whom you are talking may be in a very low consciousness and then your food will be affected. So, you should always try to remain in a high consciousness and, for that, silence will be a considerable help. It will also be of considerable help if you can be in a meditative consciousness. Otherwise, outwardly you may remain silent, but inwardly your mind will be thinking of the entire world. That kind of so-called silence does not make any sense. But to remain both inwardly and outwardly silent will help you to enter into a higher realm of consciousness.

Question: Does Indian food embody a higher consciousness than other styles?

Sri Chinmoy: Indian food does not necessarily embody a higher consciousness than other types of food. The consciousness of food depends mostly on the consciousness of the cook. It is true that food itself has its own consciousness, but since the cook is a human being, he has a more evolved consciousness than the food. So the cook can transform the consciousness of the food if it is necessary and if he wants to do so. He can add to the consciousness of the food or he can even bring the consciousness of the food into his own consciousness for enlightenment.

They say that in the West, food has very little to do with faith. In India the link between food and faith is almost inseparable. Our Upanishadic Seers cried out: "Annam Brahma"(Food is the Brahman).

Question: Do you feel that onions and garlic are tamasic or harmful to the health?

Sri Chinmoy: Onions and garlic are far from tamasic. They are rajasic; they are dynamic. Both onions and garlic, when taken in small quantity, are good. Onions help considerably in forming blood, and also they help in curing eye defects. Garlic is good for curing rheumatism. But again, everything has to be taken in moderation. If we take onions and garlic beyond proportion, then naturally it will tell upon our health.

Question: Spicy foods are often classified as rajasic. Would Indian food correctly fall under this category?

Sri Chinmoy: We cannot say that all Indian food is spicy. There are many people in India who avoid using spices or eating any hot preparations. In our own family, I like rajasic food but my brother Mantu will never go near chilli or anything hot. It depends on the individual. Some people like spicy foods; others don't. Especially in South India, people generally care for hot, spicy food more than in other parts of India. But there are many people in India who do not like hot food at all.

Question: Does the beauty of the kitchen affect the food?

Sri Chinmoy: Beauty as such is useless. It is the purity of the kitchen that affects the food. A flower is beautiful and, at the same time, it is pure. If something embodies both beauty and purity, then it will be most helpful. If you bring into the kitchen most beautiful dolls or pieces of furniture, they will be useless; they won't be of any help to the consciousness of the food. But if you bring in flowers, which have both purity and beauty, then naturally it will help the food.

Question: What makes flavour: consciousness or spices?

Sri Chinmoy: Spices have their own consciousness; again, consciousness also can spice the food. Consciousness and spices are like two friends. Nevertheless, there are many cooks in God's creation whose consciousness is worse than the worst, but they have the capacity – let us say unconsciously – to identify themselves with the consciousness of the spices. They have an instinctive feeling and, by virtue of that feeling, they know the quality and the quantity of the spices to use. Therefore, we notice a very good flavour in their preparation.

Question: Do vegetables have awareness?

Sri Chinmoy: Yes, vegetables do have awareness. They have a conscious awareness of which we ourselves are not conscious. Of course, their conscious awareness is like a kind of instinctive feeling.

Question: Is it better to rinse vegetables before or after chopping them?

Sri Chinmoy: It is advisable to rinse vegetables both before and after chopping them. Then there will be a greater sense of purity, especially in the mind of the cook. The mind is always deceptive, so in order to avoid the deceptive mind it is better to rinse the vegetables before and after they are chopped. Then the mind will be convinced that the vegetables are clean.

Question: Can you tell us some of the different occult meanings of food?

Sri Chinmoy: Bread is life. Water is consciousness. Cucumber is mildness. Onion is dynamism. Garlic is determination. Each food has its own consciousness; there is no end to the list.

Question: They say that Yogis in India eat *soma* and get some insight.

Sri Chinmoy: The *soma* the Yogis use is the juice of the *soma* plant. Only the Vedic Seers knew how to use this herb. Here in the West people are experimenting with plants, but these have nothing to do with the *soma* plants, which the ancient Seers used. Also, they do not know how the Seers used them. The process the Westerners are using now is absolutely wrong. The experiences they are having are totally counterfeit. They are ruining some of their subtle nerves. I have students who once upon a time were victims of these drugs. Now that they are living the spiritual life most sincerely, they can easily distinguish between real spiritual experiences and what they were having before.

Question: If one gets ill from food, is it usually because the cook was in a bad consciousness or is it entirely due to the quality of the food?

Sri Chinmoy: You can blame the bad consciousness of the cook, you can blame the quality of the food, and, again, you can blame your own bad consciousness. Sometimes the consciousness of the cook is very good and the consciousness of the food is very good, but the consciousness of the person who is eating is horrible. Therefore, he pays the penalty. True, sometimes the consciousness of the food is not praiseworthy or the consciousness of the cook is not praiseworthy, and therefore one may suffer from the food. But it also happens that the person who eats is in a very low consciousness. Then he will definitely suffer.

Question: Is there any connection between art appreciation and food appreciation?

Sri Chinmoy: All parts of the being can create art just by appreciating something. As soon as we appreciate somebody or something, we are creating art. Our appreciation itself is a form of beauty, a creative capacity or a form of art. Our appreciation becomes an act of offering. Offering is creation and creation is art. Even in eating food, if we appreciate the food, immediately our appreciation itself is a form of art, because our appreciation is giving life to the thing that we are eating. Otherwise, it is all lifeless. When we see a flower, when we appreciate the flower, immediately we add beauty to the flower. If we use our third eye, we shall see that the flower is already beautiful; but the moment we appreciate it, our appreciation becomes an added life to the beauty of the flower itself. So every part of us, if we use it properly, can create a form of art.

Books are food for the mind.
Love of concern is food for the heart.
Bliss of oneness is food for the soul.

Question: How is it that some advanced people do not have to eat at all?

Sri Chinmoy: If people are advanced in age, they do not have to give out as much energy as they did during their youth. At that time, they did much more on the physical plane. Naturally, when one has to offer more on the physical plane, the physical itself needs more sustenance. But when people become old, from the physical point of view they do not offer much to the world at large. Therefore, they do not have to eat much.

People who are spiritually advanced don't have to eat much if they don't want to. If they want to live on earth with very little food, then the Peace that they bring down from above will help them considerably. Their inner food can easily sustain them even if they eat very little material food. They can maintain themselves in this way if they want to. But if they want to remain on earth in a normal, natural way, eating material food, then they will take help from material food. It entirely depends on the individual choice.

Believe it or not,
My morning meal
Is freedom-sky.
Try to believe;
Who knows,
You may succeed today.

Believe it or not,
My afternoon meal
Is love-sun.
Try to believe;
Who knows,
You may succeed tomorrow.

Believe it or not,
My evening meal
Is peace-moon.
Try to believe;
Who knows,
You may succeed
In the near future
Or
Someday.

Benefits of vegetarian diet

Question: What should one eat in the spiritual life?

Sri Chinmoy: The kind of food that keeps the body and mind calm and quiet is the best food for those following the spiritual life. Naturally, vegetables are far better than meat. Meat comes from the animals, which are always fighting and destroying one another. If we eat meat, then the animal consciousness enters into us. And it is this animal consciousness that we want to transcend. But the consciousness of vegetables and fruits is very mild. They are not destructive like animals.

The mild qualities of vegetables, on the other hand, help us to establish in our inner life as well as in our outer life, the qualities of sweetness, softness, simplicity and purity.

Question: How important is it for a spiritual person to follow a vegetarian diet? Is it absolutely essential?

Sri Chinmoy: The answer will be yes and no. It depends on the individual aspirant. We all know that we have come from the animal kingdom. We believe in reincarnation. So once upon a time, we were all animals. Now, we have come into the human creation and we are progressing and evolving and all of us will realise God on the strength of our aspiration.

For an aspirant, it is advisable to be a vegetarian precisely because when he eats meat, the aggressive quality of the animal enters into him. We are trying to live a life of peace and tranquillity. If we sincerely want that kind of life, then it is foolishness on our part to eat something that would diminish our peace and tranquillity and stand in the way of our meditation, concentration, etc. So it is always advisable to accept the vegetarian life. But, again, there are some countries or some parts of the world where it is exceptionally cold and there it is impossible for those particular people, to live on vegetables alone. What are they going to do then? There only if they eat meat can they remain on earth. Then, again, there are some sincere seekers whose physical constitution is very weak. Some children, for example, who are very ill require meat for a short time to regain their strength. Others from the beginning of their lives have been eating meat and now they have formed such a habit, such a bad habit, you can say, that they cannot manage without it even for a day. What are they going to do? On the one hand, they have sincere aspiration, genuine aspiration, but their body revolts. I feel, in such rare cases, that they should eat meat.

But as a general rule, it is always advisable to be a vegetarian because we are trying to throw away the animal qualities and propensities from our nature. Already when we go deep within, we see that we have two different qualities or natures; the divine and the undivine. The undivine is the animal in us and the animal within us will always be aggressive and destructive. The divine in us will always be progressive and illumined. So if we want to march and run towards our Goal, then we have to do away with our animal life. To do that, whatever animal qualities we take into us in the form of meat or in some other form have to be discontinued.

Now to come back to your question, if one says that one has to be a vegetarian in order to realise God or that one cannot achieve God-realisation unless he is a vegetarian, then I say that it is pure foolishness. There are many meat-eaters who have realised God: Christ, Vivekananda and many others who realised God, but ate meat as others do. There are many. A few months ago someone told me that in order to have purity in abundance, he stopped eating meat, but he also felt that just by becoming a vegetarian, he would be able to realise God. He would not have to meditate, he would not have to concentrate; only by becoming a vegetarian, he could achieve union with the Absolute. So

I told him that in India, all widows without exception are forbidden to take meat. When their husbands die, on that very day, they have to stop taking meat. Now in spite of my deepest love and respect for Indian widows, I don't think that they are all God-realised souls. That kind of feeling towards the vegetarian life is absurd. Yet we have to strike a balance. For a sincere aspirant, it is certainly advisable and helpful to be a vegetarian.

Question: I find that when I eat meat I cannot meditate very well; I feel restless. But if I don't eat meat, I feel very weak.

Sri Chinmoy: You know very well that animals are restless, aggressive, destructive and unevolved. We have transcended the animal consciousness to some extent, and we have come out of the animal kingdom. We are only one step ahead on the ladder of evolution, but the difference between an animal and a human being is very vast. Now, when you eat something, naturally you will absorb the qualities of that thing. What you have within you will unavoidably manifest itself outwardly in some way. When you eat meat, the immediate result is restlessness, aggressive and destructive impulses and thoughts, and lowering of the consciousness.

It is not true, however, that if you do not eat meat you will lose strength, power or energy. There are millions of people on earth who do not eat meat, but who are physically very strong and healthy. You may say that your constitution is different from theirs, but I wish to say that in God's creation there is something called inner food. What is this food? It is Peace, Light, Bliss and all other divine, fulfilling qualities. When you aspire properly, concentrate properly, meditate properly, you will be able to draw this inner food into your body. It may take quite a number of years for you to attain this degree of inner proficiency, but in the meantime try to go deep within and see what actually gives you most of your strength. I have known people to claim it is meat that gives them strength, but when they go deep within, they discover that it is their own feeling and idea about meat that is giving them strength.

You can change that idea and feel that it is not meat but the spiritual energy pervading your body that gives you strength. That energy comes from meditation and aspiration as well as from proper nourishment. The strength you get from aspiration and meditation is infinitely more powerful than the strength you get from meat and fish, so these things can easily be omitted from your diet.

You are practising meditation most sincerely and most devotedly. What you have to do is get rid of the idea that meat gives you strength. That idea is so deeply rooted in your mind that now you cannot separate yourself from it. But the moment you are totally freed from that idea, you will see that it is not principally meat that gives you strength; it is wholesome food in general, as well as the proper mental attitude and spiritual aspiration.

Question: How do the animal qualities that we get from meat actually affect us? What is the process?

Sri Chinmoy: Inside us there are always some negative forces. When negative forces from the outer world – restlessness, wrong thoughts and emotional urges – enter into us, immediately the unlit emotion that we already have in the lower vital comes to the fore and responds to the wrong forces that have entered into us. Then the negative forces that are inside and the wrong forces that are coming from the outside join together and we become their victim.

Restlessness, negative forces, vital forces have their root in the navel. When we concentrate on the navel for five minutes, our will becomes powerful and direct like an arrow, and the wrong forces come under our control. They see the power of our concentration: they see that we are going to cut them asunder if they create any problems. If we can keep the wrong forces that are already inside us under control, then the forces that come from eating meat will not be able to cause restlessness.

But I wish all my disciples eventually to stop eating meat. If you do, your aspiration will be better. Otherwise, what happens is that you generally do not get subtle experiences, subtle visions, subtle realisations. Of course, there were some spiritual Masters like Vivekananda and others who did eat meat. But they could do it because they were like roaring lions in the spiritual world. They were not disturbed by the forces within the meat.

I do not want to impose a strict vegetarian diet on my disciples; it is a matter of individual choice. And if a doctor advises someone that it is absolutely necessary for him to eat meat and fish for a short period of time, he has to do it. But, in general, if you want the Absolute, the Highest, Self-realisation, you should stop eating meat and fish. If you can, do it today. If it takes one year or ten years or twenty years, do it gradually. Once you are realised, you can eat meat and fish if you want. But right now I must say that the animal consciousness in meat will not allow the sincere, dedicated aspirant to enter into the highest and deepest consciousness.

Question: From the spiritual point of view, is eating fish as harmful as eating meat?

Sri Chinmoy: Fish is worse than meat. Animals, by nature, are aggressive, but at the same time animal life-blood is very powerful and strong. In the animal consciousness there is some dynamic push forward. It may be undirected and wild, but at least there is some dynamic push forward. An animal runs here and there; it does not want to remain satisfied. This dynamic quality can energise us to some extent. But when it enters into the human consciousness, it also creates problems. Its restlessness disturbs our purity, our peace of mind.

The least harmful kind of meat to eat is lamb. The lamb is quite mild, whereas other animals are more aggressive. Also, chicken will not be as harmful as red meat. It is not good to eat any kind of meat, but if one cannot stop, it is better to eat meat than fish.

Spiritually, the fish is less evolved than the animal. An animal runs here and there; it does not remain satisfied. But a fish is a creature of sloth, inertia, sluggishness, impurity and inconscience. Inertia is its satisfaction, meanness is its satisfaction, and next to meanness is death's world. When we are bound by meanness, immediately death comes to us and binds us more. The consciousness of a fish immediately enters into the mud of inconscience and lifelessness. Although you may feel that a fish is innocent, humble and mild, these qualities are only on the surface. Its inner qualities are meanness, inertia, sloth and darkness itself. There is no feeling in fish for progress.

If you want to eat fish or if you must eat fish, please try to eat small fish, rather than large fish. Small fish at times want to open consciously or unconsciously to the light. But large fish never want to open to the light either consciously or unconsciously; they shut out the light.

Question: What about eggs and milk and other dairy products?

Sri Chinmoy: Dairy products are fine. They do no harm because they do not have that kind of destructive vibration. But those who practise Kundalini Yoga and want to open the spiritual centres should not eat dairy products either. If one wants to open any of the six major centres, dairy products are harmful because they prevent the centres from opening. But if one wants the inner experience of Peace, Light and Bliss and does not care for the opening of the chakras, he can eat any dairy product.

Question: I read in a macrobiotic book that potatoes and tomatoes are bad to eat. I wonder if you could tell me if this is true.

Sri Chinmoy: From my own experience I know that one can safely eat any vegetable if one wants to. I assure you, there is nothing at all wrong with eating potatoes or tomatoes. The only important distinction is that between meat and vegetables.

To the end of my life, I will speak ill of so-called *healthy food* that has no sugar, no salt, no oil and no taste. Too much sugar is not good, I agree. But food also has to give the mind joy.

The mind plays an important role in our physical well-being. People today are turning towards a vegetarian diet because animals eat so much rubbish. But when we eat vegetables, the mind has to feel that we are eating something very solid and nourishing. The mind has to feel that the vegetables have some strength in them. As soon as we think of cauliflower or potato, for example, the mind gets a sense of something solid. But if we think of a leafy vegetable like spinach or cabbage, at that time the mind does not get a feeling of strength. When we think of the leaf-consciousness, all our strength goes away.

The term 'salad', for example, will never give us the feeling of strength, but today everybody is eating salad. The fat man eats salad to lose weight and the thin man eats salad in order not to get fat. Unfortunately, the fat man is still gaining weight! If we want to get the utmost nourishment from salad, immediately from the word itself the idea has to enter into our mind that it is all-nourishing, that it is like a medicine that will cure all diseases.

Even the term 'bread' has real strength in it because down through the centuries bread has represented something very solid to the mind. The same is true of rice. If we say the word 'rice', immediately our whole being is satisfied. When we say 'bread' or 'rice', from head to foot we get some satisfaction. From the soles of our feet to the crown of our head, like an electric current there is the feeling that we are really eating something good. When we say 'bread and butter', the word 'butter' is not adding anything; it adds only fatness! But as soon as we say 'bread', our whole being is immediately nurtured.

Question: What kind of food should we eat to achieve purity?

Sri Chinmoy: Please try to avoid meat and fish; and, of course, liquor and tobacco are out of the question. All fruits and vegetables, as well as dairy products, are fine. Processed foods may also be eaten as long as they do not interfere with good health.

Also, coffee and tea are not good, except for herbal teas. To me, coffee and tea are slow poison. They just take a little longer time to kill you. Of course, each person has some power of resistance, so if it is a very slow poison, if we fight we can win the battle. But we must not squander our power by using it to fight against these slow poisons.

Question: What is the best way to become a vegetarian if one is accustomed to eating meat and fish?

Sri Chinmoy: The safest, surest way is to start gradually. A disciple of mine used to drink tea six times a day, so I asked him to drink it five times, then after a month I told him to reduce it to four times. Eventually he stopped completely. Serious things must be done gradually. If he had stopped all at once, he might have suffered from some serious disease. If the body is not strong, any sudden change in its habits can cause a serious attack upon one's health.

Question: Why are eggs acceptable to some vegetarians and not others?

Sri Chinmoy: Again, it depends on the individual. If one is fussy and says that eggs come from an animal, then naturally he will try to shun the animal consciousness in eggs. The egg comes from the chicken and the chicken comes from the egg, so the story repeats itself; it is all animal consciousness from that point of view. But if one wants to separate the consciousness, saying that in eggs one doesn't see the immediate presence of the animal consciousness, then one can take eggs. It entirely depends on how the individual regards eggs and the creatures that produce eggs. Everything is in the mind. The mind tells us that something is harmful or that something is not harmful. Sometimes there is great truth in what the mind says, for there are things that can be really harmful. Again, there are some things which the mind rejects that are not at all harmful.

Question: I am a vegetarian but I work as a meat handler. Is this increasing my karma?

Sri Chinmoy: If you are a vegetarian, and if your earthly duty demands that you work at a place where you have to handle meat, do not feel that you are increasing your karma or doing something wrong. As long as you do not feel the necessity of eating meat, and your consciousness is not in the aggressive animal consciousness, then there is no harm.

Sometimes, I know, there is something called compulsion. If this is the only place that you can get a job, then you should do it. But your consciousness must not be in the meat; your consciousness must be in something pure and divine. You have to know where your consciousness remains while you work. There are some people in the spiritual life who do not eat meat, but when they see meat and fish immediately their greed and desire comes to the fore. This kind of vegetarianism is only self-deception. But if you do not want to eat meat and do not feel the need of it, then even if you touch meat there will be no problem.

If you are extremely sincere, and if you feel that touching meat lowers your consciousness, then your sincere aspiration will knock at God's Door and God will provide you with some other job. If He feels that your consciousness is being lowered by touching meat and if you are sincerely crying and searching for another job, then He will not allow you to remain with this one. But if your consciousness is not lowered, then God will say, "There is no harm in it."

Question: I have an excessive passion for eating. I love the taste of food. How can I control this passion?

Sri Chinmoy: Everyone, every seeker, every aspirant, every disciple, eventually has to conquer all passion. Now, passion is a very complicated thing. It can be in the lower vital, it can be in the mind or it can be in the heart. This passion is persistent. But once you are purified in the physical, in the vital and in the mind, then the passion can easily be conquered.

Now you say that your problem is food. If your passion for eating takes you away from your spiritual life, from your inner discipline, then naturally you should try to cut down. Many people follow a spiritual path but are content to make very little progress. But if you want to make the best progress, the highest progress, then in your spiritual life you have to give up things that you eat only for the sake of taste.

I don't know what food you actually prefer. Suppose you are eating too much meat. Naturally you will have to feel that this meat is disturbing your inner peace. Meat is not good for the spiritual life. You have to know what meat actually does, how it harms you. Meat comes from the animal world. We see animals quarrelling and fighting all the time. We don't want to be animals any more. We have already evolved out of the animal kingdom. But the restless, agitated quality that you get from meat is bound to express itself through your outer actions. Now, if you have been eating meat all your life, then I will be the last person to tell you to give up eating meat all at once. But gradually, gradually you can cut down the amount. Then you will come to a point when you have to give up meat altogether if you want to make the fastest progress.

We have to take food in order to keep our body fit. We can drink milk, we can take vegetables, we can take eggs, we can take so many things besides meat. If we eat vegetables and other foods, they will not harm us in our spiritual life.

When you are asking about controlling passions, you are asking a very spiritual question. Spiritual people have to deal with food in a different way from a gluttonous, voracious eater, a greedy person who eats to please his tongue. A spiritual person, an aspirant, will eat primarily to keep his body fit. He knows that if he takes mild food, vegetables and so forth, this will help him to conquer his passions. At the same time he is offering to the body the food which the body legitimately demands. If the body becomes one with the divine Consciousness, then naturally it will try to fulfil God the way God wants to be fulfilled. God has given us a variety of foods and it is we who have to know what food we should take in order to expedite our spiritual progress. But again, how fast do you want to go? If you are content to go slowly, you can continue to take the food that you are taking now since you are fond of it. Try to diminish the quantity; in that way you can progress slowly. But the important thing is to start.

Whatever you feel is wrong in your life, whether it is passion or something else, try to minimise it and gradually it will be totally eliminated. You have to start from where you are standing and one day you will reach your goal. If you feel that it is too difficult, then it will always remain impossible. But if you feel that it is not only possible but practicable, then soon you will see that it is not only possible and practicable, but inevitable. You can do it, you are bound to do it and you will do it.

> *The food is ready.*
> *The waiter is ready.*
> *The table is ready.*
> *The eater is ready.*
> *Only one thing is not ready:*
> *The hunger, the real hunger,*
> *The inner hunger*
> *In the eater.*

95

Food and consciousness

Question: How are nutrition and consciousness interrelated?

Sri Chinmoy: Consciousness has nutrition itself; again, nutrition has consciousness itself. But consciousness has infinitely more power to add to nutrition than nutrition has to add to consciousness. Consciousness can invoke cosmic energy, but nutrition as such cannot invoke cosmic energy to add to consciousness.

> *I eat to live.*
> *Indeed, this is my wisdom-light.*
> *I live to eat.*
> *Indeed, this is my ignorance-night.*

Question: What kind of prayer or meditation should we offer before eating food?

Sri Chinmoy: Only invoke the Supreme and repeat His Name. You are eating food not to become the strongest man on earth. You are eating so that you can maintain your health. You are eating in order to become a good instrument, a perfect instrument of the Supreme. After you have eaten, you have energised your being. You have to energise the body so that you can become a perfect instrument of the Supreme.

Question: Why should we meditate on our food before eating it?

Sri Chinmoy: Before eating, it is obligatory to meditate. Before doing anything it is advisable for a spiritual person to meditate, to think of the Inner Pilot, the Supreme. The Supreme comes before everything we do, He is in the middle of everything we do, and He is at the end of everything we do. If we meditate before we eat, then His Compassion descends on us, and His Compassion is nothing short of energising power. So, along with the material food, if we can receive energising power, then naturally we will get double benefit from the food.

Question: How soon can one eat before meditating?

Sri Chinmoy: If you want to meditate after eating a full meal such as lunch or dinner, you should wait at least two and a half hours. If you have had a very light breakfast, you can meditate after an hour and a half. Before that you will not have a deep, true meditation because your subtle nerves will be very heavy and sluggish. The major cords – *Ida, Pingala* and *Sushumna* – find it extremely difficult to allow the cosmic energy to pass through them if the body has just taken a full meal.

If you want to meditate most sincerely, it is always advisable to meditate on an empty stomach. Now, empty does not mean totally empty. If you are pinched with hunger, eat something very light: otherwise, your hunger will disturb your meditation. You can have a cup of juice or water. And after meditation, you should try to wait for at least half an hour before you eat, for it takes this amount of time to assimilate the spiritual forces that you have received.

Question: Isn't it true that the body affects our ability to concentrate? Wouldn't some kind of diet and purification be helpful?

Sri Chinmoy: Certainly, it is true to some extent. But the main thing is one's consciousness. Merely becoming a vegetarian will not purify or elevate the consciousness in any way. One may bathe ten times a day and achieve the utmost in outer physical purity, but if he does not aspire, this bathing will not take him even one step forward toward God. Again, somebody else may not bathe more than once a day, but if his aspiration is very lofty, he will run toward his goal with utmost inner purity. Certainly, purification of the body does help, but if one wants to get utmost spiritual help, it is purification of the consciousness which is important, and not diet or cleanliness or exercise.

Question: What is meant by "*Annam Brahma*", Food is God?

Sri Chinmoy: Food is life and life is God. Again, God is life. Food gives us new life; it energises us. Anything that energises us is life – the stream of life – and life is God.

Food has God. God is food.
Food has life. God is life.
Food has reality. God is reality.
Food has sound-success.
God is sound-success.
Food has silence-progress.
God is silence-progress.

Question: How can we always feel that food is God?

Sri Chinmoy: When you pray and meditate, you are bound to feel that you are devouring God's Peace, Love and Light. Again, when you are eating material food, if you feel that this food is keeping you alive and in good health, which enables you to pray and meditate, then naturally you can keep both food and God in mind. When you pray, you feel that God is coming to you in the form of Peace, Light and Bliss, which is your real food. Again, while you are eating material food, you feel that God in the form of this food is keeping you alive. At that time, food really helps you to think of your Beloved Supreme. Therefore, both food and God can easily be seen as one.

Losing weight and fasting

My Lord, I long to take from You
Many lessons.
May my first lesson be in losing
My heavy ignorance-weight.

Question: If a person is overweight, does it affect his consciousness?

Sri Chinmoy: If you are really heavy beyond necessity, your consciousness carries a heavy load. Lethargy enters into you most powerfully. When you lose unnecessary weight, excessive weight, your outer capacity increases and your inner beauty comes forward and grows in the physical.

Question: When you are fat and you lose weight, is that any help to the soul?

Sri Chinmoy: Losing weight does help the soul, because the mind becomes clear. When one loses weight, when the body becomes light, the mind does not have that heavy pressure. Again, many spiritual Masters of the highest order were unimaginably, unbelievably fat. India's Troilanga Swami was one of those. Again, some were thinner than the thinnest. In terms of physical fatness, the Jain Master Mahavira and the Lord Buddha were also not thin. God-realisation does not depend on physical fitness or fatness. But, to be perfectly frank, if you are fit and not fat, it helps the mind considerably to start decreasing its normal train of thoughts. At that time the mind does not become jealous or impure. In this way, physical fitness does help the mind, and if the mind becomes clear, the mind is likely to listen to the soul, which it often does not do when it is clouded.

So, to come back to your question, it helps to lighten the mind by losing weight. Again, I am telling you that fatness has nothing to do with the soul, but it has to do with the physical proper, the mind and vital. If the vital and mind are under control, then it is infinitely easier to realise the soul. Physical fitness has nothing to do with the soul, but physical fitness can help the mind. If the mind is in a better frame of consciousness, then definitely the mind can be of tremendous help to the soul. The heart is always eager to be of service to the soul, always. But one day the mind tries to be of service to the soul, and then it may take weeks, months or years for the mind once again to be of any service to the soul.

Question: I fasted for six days, and now I feel more inner peace and that a lot of wrong forces have left me. Is there a connection between fasting or losing weight and wrong forces leaving the body?

Sri Chinmoy: Losing weight is good, but you cannot say that the thinnest people are the most pure people on earth! Some people carry extra weight, absolutely unnecessary weight. If they lose weight, then along with their physical lightness, the mind becomes lighter and more clarity enters into the mind. Another thing is cheerfulness. Let us say you are carrying 20 or 30 pounds extra, and then you lose it. How much cheerfulness enters your mind! When cheerfulness enters into the mind, it destroys many negative forces. If you are cheerful, many, many lower vital forces you can conquer. Cheerfulness has tremendous, tremendous strength. So from that point of view, it is true that if you lose weight, wrong forces leave you, but you cannot say that just by losing weight all lower forces will be conquered.

Question: Does being fit help one's spiritual height?

Sri Chinmoy: If you are proportionate, if your weight is perfect, it adds to your spiritual height. Spiritual Peace, Light and Bliss do not increase your stomach. Don't think of Indian spiritual Masters. We are notorious. All spiritual Masters except one or two have had a wonderful stomach. There is no wisdom there. If we don't take exercise, if we don't pay any attention to what we eat, then how are we going to manifest in the physical? Inwardly we are everything, but in the matter of exercise, we are nothing. It is very unfortunate that many of the spiritual Masters are really great but they don't exercise. Again, they realised God and they will say who cares for earth and the physical being. I will reply: True, your soul will take you to God, your aspiration will tell you about God, but what are you going to do for God? If your body is in a good consciousness, then your earth consciousness, which is in the physical, gets inspiration to lead a higher, better life.

If we meditate before we eat, then His Compassion descends on us, and His Compassion is nothing short of energising power. Along with the material food, if we can receive energising power, then naturally we will get double benefit from the food.

Queston: How can I lose weight?

Sri Chinmoy: Somebody went to a doctor and asked how to lose weight. The doctor said, "Eat as much as you can for as long as you can."

The person said, "Then how am I going to lose weight?"

The doctor said, "If you eat too much, then you are not going to get up. You will just lie in bed all the time. Then you won't go to work and your boss will fire you. If your boss fires you, you will have no money to buy food. Then automatically you will lose weight!"

To lose weight, do not have a long-range goal. Say you have to lose forty pounds. Never think of forty pounds. Only think of five pounds as your goal. You cannot climb up the Himalayas overnight.

Exercise

Losing weight

You can meditate every day to lose weight. As soon as you start meditating, you have to think of yourself as a feather. You can keep a feather in front of you and feel that you are that feather. Use your imagination-power. Imagination is reality in another world. If your concentrative will-power is focussed on that feather, and if you can become one with the feather-consciousness, no matter what you eat, you will be able to lose weight. Your goal is not to become as light as a feather – far from it! The feather is only symbolic. The feather symbolises lightness. If you can keep inside your mind a fixed idea that you are light, automatically the mind will put pressure on the physical. Imagination is a very strong power. Your imagination will be able to help you.

Question: What is your view on fasting?

Sri Chinmoy: If you are not under the guidance of a spiritual Master or following a specific path, and if you are studying a few books and trying to discipline your life on your own, then in that case fasting is advisable. If you fast once or twice a month, it will purify your subtle nerves. Purity is of great importance in the spiritual life. But this purity does not come from fasting only. We also have to meditate properly. We have to offer our inner life to God. Then only will our outer life be properly purified and transformed. In addition to our inner prayer and meditation, if we fast twice a month or three times a month, it will aid us in purifying the body's outer existence. It will also aid us in our concentration and meditation. But if somebody fasts three times a week or four times a week, then that person is making a serious mistake. Fasting two or three times a week will only weaken our system.

It is through aspiration, not fasting, that we reach our goal. In order to increase our inner cry we have to meditate regularly and devotedly. If we meditate, then purification is bound to come. Fasting is not indispensable in the spiritual life. Only aspiration, our inner cry is indispensable. If we know how to aspire, then our nature will be purified. Then, in our meditation and contemplation we get the results of fasting.

Question: Please tell me if we are in better contact with the Divine when we are fasting – drinking only juice and water. Does fasting help us to realise God?

Sri Chinmoy: When you drink juice you are not fasting. Many people say, "Early in the morning I drink a cup of coffee, and at noon I have a glass of juice, and in the evening only a glass of milk." This is their idea of fasting. But to me that is not fasting. In true fasting, you can have only pure water and nothing else.

If you decide to fast, you have to know why you are doing it. If you feel that by fasting you will realise God, it is foolishness. The real name of God is Delight and Joy. If your Father is all Joy, will He ask you to torture yourself in order to come to Him? God is the possessor of boundless Joy, and we know that He is also infinitely compassionate. He gave you the body – it is His body – and if you start torturing His body, will He be pleased? Never! If you start fasting for God-realisation, God will say that you are walking on the wrong path.

But fasting can help us reduce weight, cure some of our physical ailments and purify our nerves and mind. Very often we eat unwholesome food, and the poor body needs some rest and purification. Also, when we look at undivine people and things, their vibrations enter into us from the atmosphere and affect our physical body – the skin, the muscles, the nerves. If we want to fast one day a month to purify our system, it is advisable. We need purity to appreciate God's existence on earth. It is in purity – pure thoughts, pure deeds, pure consciousness – that God abides. Fasting can help us to a great extent in self-purification. And when purity enters into us, we go faster towards our God-realisation. But this is only the first step; fasting alone will not give us God-realisation.

Losing weight does help the soul, because the mind becomes clear.

So for purification you can try fasting – drinking only water – once a month. Now, I am only speaking from the spiritual point of view. I know nothing about your physical constitution. If you are strong and healthy you can fast; otherwise it is not advisable. But even if you don't fast, if you are a sincere seeker you can, once a week, reduce the amount of food you take. This can be done especially on Sundays, when you do not have to be very active. On Sunday most people get up late in the morning, so they can easily forget about breakfast. At lunch time they can say, "Every day I eat. If just today I eat a little less, it will not hurt me at all." Then in the evening, at dinner, they can say, "At lunch time I did not eat the usual amount, and it did me no harm. I am still quite energetic. Why not do the same now?" So once a week, on Sundays especially, if you can lighten your meals it will help you enormously. And you need not undergo a severe, torturing fast, which real spiritual figures do not recommend.

Question: If fasting really helps us to purify ourselves, then why shouldn't we fast more often than once or twice a month?

Sri Chinmoy: Fasting from time to time does help purify our body. It gives our body and our subtle nerves a kind of rest. This resting of the nerves gives us a sense of purification, for our subtle nerves play a considerable part in our Self-realisation. But if we fast too often it will just weaken our nerves and body, so instead of helping us in our God-realisation, it will hamper our inner progress.

The Buddha taught us the middle path, the path of moderation. He tried the extreme path of fasting and extreme austerity, but found it was not satisfactory. If we starve our organs, do you think we are going toward God? No! Everything should be moderate. We should use each thing for a divine purpose, for a divine cause.

Question: I can't meditate unless my body is satisfied. When I am hungry or upset, I really can't meditate.

Sri Chinmoy: If you are upset or even if you are hungry or thirsty, it is natural that you will not be able to meditate well. That is why we need perfection of the physical also. The body has to be calm and poised. Inside the body, the outer wall, is the soul. The outer temple has to be maintained. The physical has to be taken care of properly in order for good meditation to be possible. Kalidasa's great epic, *Kumar Sambhaba*, reads, "*Shariramadyam khalu* – The body is, indeed, the first instrument for spiritual discipline." Therefore, the body cannot be neglected. We must pay attention to the needs of the body, but we must not take all the body's demands as necessities. If we become the slaves of our bodies, we will never be able to meditate.

Question: In many religions, people try to make their bodies suffer. They believe in the suffering of the body. According to my understanding, these people who are trying to make their bodies suffer feel they will increase their meditation capacity this way.

Sri Chinmoy: Some people are torturing themselves to please God. I am not at all in favour of this approach. Suppose, at this moment, I am asking you to play the role of God, and I am telling you that I love you and I want to come to you. Now, shall I cut my head or arms or legs to prove to you how much I love you? No! On the contrary, I shall run towards you as fast as possible. Then, either I shall sit at your feet or I shall embrace you because I love you. If I take you as someone who is infinitely higher and better than I am, then I will go and sit at your feet. And if I take you as my dearest friend, my oneness-friend, then I will embrace you. If I cut or injure myself to prove how much I love you, you will only feel sorry for me. I must run towards you as fast as possible to prove how much I love you.

This body is a temple, and inside the temple is a shrine, which is our love for God. If we destroy the temple, then the shrine will also be ruined. So we should keep the body fit instead of torturing the body. Some people do not want to eat for two or three weeks at a time. Now, some snakes eat only twice a year. In which way are these snakes better than human beings who eat two or three times a day? Of course, you and I and all human beings are higher than these snakes. We have to use our wisdom.

When Lord Buddha sat at the foot of a tree for his enlightenment, at first he said, "I am not going to eat anything." Then, when he began losing the faculties of his body, he started eating again in a normal way. Sri Ramakrishna ate three meals a day. While loving God with our body, vital, mind, heart and soul, we have to be normal. If we go to extremes and do not eat at all in order to please God, we are only torturing the body. If I love you and you also love me, will you be happy if I am suffering physically?

The child loves the mother, and the mother loves the child. Will the mother be happy if the child stops eating and ruins his whole body to prove how much he loves her? If he says, "Mother, see how much I love you; that is why I have destroyed my health," the mother will feel miserable. She will say, "If you love me, then come to me as quickly as possible." So it is advisable to follow the path of moderation and not the path of austerity. We should eat to keep our senses intact and our body in perfect condition.

There are countless people on earth who are poverty-stricken and do not get regular meals. Have all the poor people become spiritual? Have they all realised God? No! Here is the proof that if we do not eat, we are not necessarily closer to God.

Let us lead a normal life and not go to extremes. We will not be greedy, voracious eaters, nor will we lead austere lives and negate food. We have to keep the body-temple in very good condition so we will be able to worship at the shrine and please God.

The food of my eyes is scenery.
The food of my nose is fragrance.
The food of my ears is spiritual teaching.
The food of my mind is clarity.
The food of my heart is purity.
The food of my soul is Liberation.

4

The Bright and Clear Inner Weather

Mental and emotional balance

When my inner weather
Is clear,
My outer weather
Is bound to be clear as well.

There are two realities: one is happiness and the other is unhappiness. Happiness lifts us up to the skies. Unhappiness makes us infinitely more miserable than we can bear to be. But if we take God as our only Reality, then we can maintain our balance. We will see that at one point He is simply approving of something, and at another point He is eager for something to happen, because it is the manifestation of Divinity.

If we look at the negative side of life, we see unhappiness, sorrows, anxieties, fear, doubt and so on. If we look at the positive side, we see faith, love, joy, readiness, willingness, eagerness and so many other divine qualities. Now, we want to balance our life in such a way that the negative forces will not be able to conquer the positive forces. Balance means that ultimately, nothing destructive will happen, that God is always there to bring the whole world to perfection – in His own Way, at His own Time.

Balance comes from inner poise. If we do not have inner poise, there can be no balance in the outer life. But if we have inner poise, we can take the suffering, the negative side of life, as part of God's creation. God is also inside that negative aspect, and God will work inside the negative aspect of life in His own Way. If God asks us to enter into the negative, destructive aspect, we shall do so – not with fear, but with enthusiasm and eagerness.

We human beings want to have balance in our life only to have happiness. But our idea of happiness is no happiness. We feel that happiness itself will make everything balanced. No, happiness does not do that. Our way of happiness will never make our life balanced. It is only God's Way that will give us balance. Otherwise, at every moment one side of the scale – either happiness or unhappiness – will carry more weight. Only by entering into God's Heart and becoming one with God can we have a balanced mind and a balanced life. Otherwise, it is not possible. We have to see that at every moment God is keeping His own Heart-Door open. His Heart-Door is open to you, open to me, open to everybody. But if we want to enter into God's Heart, then we shall pray for His Happiness in His own Way.

Balance in the mind, balance in the heart, balance in life itself is of utmost importance. If we have balance in our inner life, we shall never be shattered by what happens in the outer life or in the inner life. At every moment confidence will come to the fore in us. On the strength of our confidence, we will be able to say: "I am of God and God is of me. And I am not only **with** God, but I am also **for** God."

Balance

Question: What is the spiritual significance of balance?

Sri Chinmoy: In the spiritual life balance is of paramount importance. When the result of an action elevates our consciousness, we feel that we are running towards our destined Goal. When our inner mounting cry takes us to the loftiest heights, our whole being becomes a sea of delight. But when we don't have outer success, it doesn't mean that we are not running towards the Highest. Sometimes defeat is a blessing in disguise. Defeat can be a reality which is secretly preparing us to run the fastest. When undivine thoughts fill our mind, we have to know that they are like passing clouds which will soon disappear. Then our soul will again come to the fore. If we have perfect balance and do not become sad or depressed, at that time we make the fastest progress. We need equanimity of mind in order to make the heart receptive. We need perfect balance in order to achieve real satisfaction.

Soulfully and powerfully invoke
Pristine peace and poise
During your daily meditation.
Once you have their tremendous
Inner strength,
The life of worry and hurry
Will be totally unknown to you.

Question: How can we have more joy and less tension in our daily life?

Sri Chinmoy: We can have more joy only in self-giving, not in demanding. When there is tension, it is because we want something to be done in our own way while others want it done in their way. Tension starts in the mind because we see light in one way and others see light in some other way. So there is no peace, no poise, only tension.

Tension also comes when we want to do something in the twinkling of an eye that takes two hours or two days to do. We have to know that God has not thought of it in that way. God wants us to take two hours or two days to achieve it. If we can keep God's Hour in our minds and not our own hour, we will get joy. Tension goes away from the seeker's mind when he knows the art of surrendering to God's Will.

We must see that God operates not only in us but in others as well. God also operates in our so-called enemies. But these are not our real enemies. Our real enemies are our doubt, fear, anxiety and worry. When we do not cry to perfect others, but only try to perfect our own lives then we will have joy. Also, if we do not expect anything from anybody else but expect everything only from God, then we will get joy. If we can feel that we are not indispensable, that without us the world can go on perfectly well, then we will have joy. This is the way we can all get abundant joy in our spiritual life.

Question: Is it more effective to pray for peace of mind or for cheerfulness when you are unhappy?

Sri Chinmoy: If you are unhappy, then pray to the Supreme for happiness. If you have restlessness, then pray for peace of mind. If you have a pain in your leg, you do not pray to God to cure your head. Your head is all right, so you pray to God to cure your leg. Here also, your disease is unhappiness. What you need to cure it is happiness. In peace of mind there is happiness, true; but peace of mind belongs to a different category. When your whole being is restless, when you can't meditate even for a fleeting second, when you are full of worries, anxieties and negative qualities, then what you need is peace of mind. If you do have real peace of mind, then naturally happiness will also be there.

You have to know where you are most affected and take care of that place first. Then afterwards you can examine the entire being. If your finger is hurt, take care of your finger. Afterwards, you can take exercise to improve the condition of your whole body. If your whole body is in perfect condition, your finger won't hurt. But when you are suffering at a particular place, try to administer medicine there.

Each cheerfulness-smile
From my heart
Gives me the strength of a lion
And the beauty and purity
Of a larger-than-the-largest
Heart-garden.

Psychic depression and vital depression

When we are assailed by worries and anxieties, we have to feel that there is an antidote. When a snake bites us we try to get cured. If the worries and anxieties of the thought-world want to enter into us and attack us, then we have to get the antidote. And the antidote is to feel inwardly God's Love for us.

We love God, but we are not sure whether God loves us. We pray to God, "Oh God, grant us this, fulfil this desire." But whether or not God loves us remains vague. But we have to start with the feeling that He loves us always infinitely more than we love ourselves. How is it possible for God to love us more than we love ourselves? The answer is that God does not doubt us as we doubt ourselves. One moment we feel that we are very strong, like a great emperor; the next moment we see a red ant and are frightened to death.

Anxiety comes when there is a gap between our existence and God's Existence. Also it comes when we don't claim God as our very own or don't care to say, "I am of God; I am for God." Worries and anxieties will go away only when we identify ourselves with something that has peace, poise, divinity and the feeling of absolute oneness. If we identify ourselves with the Inner Pilot, then we get the strength of His illumining Light. Worries come because we identify ourselves with fear. If we identify ourselves with something divine, eternal and immortal, then naturally the hidden essence and quality of that particular thing will enter into us. By worrying all the time or by thinking undivine thoughts, we will never move towards our goal. We will enter into divinity only by having positive thoughts: "I am of God. I am for God." If we think this, then there can be no worry, no anxiety.

There is psychic depression and there is vital depression. In psychic depression the individual feels that there is so much that God has asked him to do and that God Himself is trying to manifest in and through him; but the world-ignorance is not letting him manifest God. Here you are with friends and your boss is the Supreme. This boss has asked you to do something, and you are trying and He is trying in and through you. But again, there are people around you who are resisting your efforts. They claim God as their Father and He claims them as His children, but they are not receptive to God's Light. Psychic depression occurs when you know what is best and, at the same time, you are helpless. Some of your brothers and sisters who are around you know what is best for them, but they do not want to do it; they do not want to budge an inch. Again, there are some who do not know what is best for them. But you know what is best for you and also for them, and you want to do it; but you are blocked.

You know what the truth is and you want to manifest the truth. But you are helpless because the people around you and before you do not cooperate. The Supreme, or your Inner Pilot, puts pressure on you and you put pressure on yourself, but it does not help. When inner peace and inner light find it difficult to come to the fore the way the Supreme wants, at God's choice Hour, then psychic depression comes. But vital depression is different. Vital depression comes from the unfulfilled demands of pride, ego and vanity. In this depression, you wanted to do something or you wanted to fulfil some desire, but you did not succeed. You are frustrated; so immediately vital depression comes. Psychic depression is on an infinitely higher level, where your choice and God's choice are one and the same. In vital depression your choice is your desire, and this has nothing to do with God's Will. There is only you and your unfulfilled desire; here God is not involved. In psychic depression you have envisioned God's Vision; God has placed His Vision in front of you, but you are unable to transform His Vision into reality. It is not for the sake of personal gain or for ego that you wanted to succeed. No. You and God have the same aspiration, the same vision, the same goal; but it is not yet manifested. Psychic depression is the result of the unfulfilled Vision of the Supreme in and through you. It is God's Divinity that wants to manifest in and through you, but it is being delayed because the world forces, the ignorance-forces, are standing against you. God and you have become one: one aspiration, one soul, one goal. But God's Vision is not fulfilled, so you have psychic depression.

The cure for psychic depression is to surrender openly to God's Will. Aspire soulfully and constantly, and then surrender to God's Will. You may soulfully cry and cry, but sometimes after psychic depression enters, you may want to take rest. You feel it is a hopeless case, so the best thing is to give up, to surrender-not to God, but to world-ignorance. Many times it has happened that the individual knows that God and he are one, but when he sees that the Supreme in him is constantly remaining unfulfilled, then he gives up. Many spiritual Masters and many seekers give up. They try together with God, but when they think that it is a hopeless case, they give up. But this is not good. One should never give up. One has to fight to the end. Sooner or later God's Will is bound to be manifested in and through you.

Question: What causes depression?

Sri Chinmoy: We want constant success, constant progress, constant achievement and fulfilment, but in our daily life we do not get it. Each moment is an opportunity to grow into more of God's Light, Peace, Bliss and Power, but if we misuse that opportunity, immediately the negative forces such as doubt, fear, jealousy, worry and depression enter into us.

We have to know what we actually want. If we want light and only light, we have to know where that light is. That light is in our peace of mind, in the tranquillity of our heart. When we unveil our inner peace, we will see that our life is all achievement and fulfilment: achievement in the process of infinite achievement, fulfilment in the process of infinite fulfilment. If we don't do that, we are bound to be the prince of depression.

What causes depression? Our acceptance of ignorance as our very own. We cannot go beyond it: we are caught; we are in the little self of ignorance, so we become depressed. But if we feel that we do not represent ignorance, we are not ignorance, we are not of ignorance and we are not for ignorance, but we are in light and we want to grow into deeper and deepest light, into all-fulfilling Light; then there can be no depression. The light which is the result of our sincere aspiration will immediately burn our depression into ashes, or it will transform our depression into constant aspiration.

Balance comes from inner poise. If we do not have inner poise, there can be no balance in the outer life.

We have to know that by being depressed we should not expect either God's Grace, or God's Love, or even sympathy from humanity. If I am depressed and a friend of mine comes to console me and sympathise with me, in that way the root of depression will not be cut. On the contrary, my depression will be nourished. Depression comes because we do not want to live in the truth; we want to live consciously or unconsciously in ignorance or, I should say, pleasure. This so-called pleasure is bound to be followed by depression. If we can identify with the soul's inner joy, which is spontaneous, we will always

have joy within us and without us. Let us try to remain in the soul's spontaneous joy.

Question: How can we overcome depression?

Sri Chinmoy: The moment you are depressed, try to feel consciously that you have imposed a heavy burden or load on your shoulders. You have to feel that you are a runner and there is a goal for you. You have to run towards your goal. The faster you run, the sooner you will reach the goal. Now, if you deliberately and consciously place something heavy on your shoulders, then naturally your speed will be very slow. So do not be unwise; you have entered into this race. Again, this race is not competition with somebody else, it is only competition against yourself and against the undivine forces: depression, doubt, fear, jealousy and all the other negative forces.

The moment depression enters into your mind or vital, please feel that there is a heavy load on your shoulders. Then naturally you will try to get rid of it because you want to run the fastest. You will discard it, just throw it aside, and then you will run towards your destined goal as fast as you can.

We can free ourselves from depression with the light within us. When we meditate on light, light comes either from above or from within. We must bring light to the fore. Our heart is very vast. The spiritual heart, not the physical heart, is larger than the universe, and abundant light is inside that heart.

If we want to climb a mountain that is very tall, we have to know our capacity. If we are weak and we want to climb the mountain all at once, we will be doomed to disappointment. We have to climb up a little and then take rest. Then we climb up a little more and rest again before we go on. If we try to climb the mountain all at once, we may ruin our capacity. We can either overestimate or underestimate our capacity. When we underestimate ourselves, depression comes. If we have the capacity to climb up three or four miles, but feel, "I cannot do it; I can only climb a little," then we are depressed because we feel that we have no capacity. But when we overestimate our capacity, we also become depressed because we cannot accomplish what we expected to accomplish. It is always better to aim just an inch higher or lower than our capacity. If we expect too much or too little, depression will come.

The best way to free ourselves from depression is to bring light forward and illumine it. If that is difficult, then take depression as something quite unimportant that is a little bit dirty and throw it away. By dwelling on it, we can't conquer it. It will come back again and again to bother us if we give it undue importance. For two days or two months we will be free, but again it will come back unless and until it is illumined.

The easiest and most effective way to conquer all negative forces, including depression, is to smile inwardly and outwardly with a sincere smile. Smile inwardly and outwardly at your enemy and say, "Oh, you have come. I am ready to conquer you." If this smile is sincere and soulful, you cannot lose. The greatest strength you have is your inner joy, and this inner joy comes only from faith – faith that whatever is best for you will come from the Supreme. What is best for you can be absolutely the worst thing for somebody else, and what is best for that person can be the worst thing for you. What you really need – not what you want but what you need – the Supreme is bound to give you.

If you know that you have taken poison, you have to take the antidote, which is cheerfulness. You can do this through gratitude, by remembering that once upon a time you were cheerful, and by

remembering what cheerfulness did to help you. So if you take depression as poison, then you will let cheerfulness come to you again. If you are cheerful, then you make progress. You cannot say that you are making very good progress just because you are suffering. You cannot say that everybody will sympathise with you and give you illumination just because you have a heavy load on your shoulders. First, they will observe whether the load is self-imposed or not. Then they will immediately see that you have thrust it upon yourself. So cheerfulness is the way, for it is cheerfulness that expedites our progress.

Question: If we are constantly going through different moods, how can we conquer depression?

Sri Chinmoy: In your case, it is not all depression. You may be thirty percent depressed, thirty percent angry and also have fear, doubt, jealousy and other things. But the strength of the soul's will is far greater than the strength of these undivine forces. If you can bring forward even one percent of your soul's willpower, with that you will be able to conquer your depression. Although you suffer for half an hour with depression, with the power of the soul's will, you can easily nullify your depression. If you can bring your willpower forward, your depression will be over in one second.

Question: I know that frustration and feeling sorry for oneself are wrong forces, yet I feel sad quite often.

Sri Chinmoy: First of all let us deal with frustration. Frustration is undoubtedly bad. Any kind of frustration is a precursor of destruction. It is not frustration that is destroyed, but frustration that destroys. If frustration were destroyed, then we would again have the life of cheerfulness. But that is not what happens.

Now the feeling of sorrow. Suppose we think about a person in our family who has passed away. For a few hours we feel sad because we miss the person who loved us or whom we loved. We feel that in our sad, sorrowful mood we are intensifying our oneness with that particular deceased person. This feeling is not bad because first we are intensifying our oneness and then we can bring down peace, light and bliss. But again, if we can maintain our oneness with that person's soul wherever it is, and feel its presence within us, then we need not feel sad even for one minute.

There is another way in which the spiritual Masters approach this case. When Sri Ramakrishna's nephew passed away, Sri Ramakrishna cried bitterly. Why was he so sad? Sri Ramakrishna felt sorrow not actually for the loss of the person but for the failure of that person to accomplish what he came on earth to accomplish. This soul had something to offer but could not do it because of the intervention of wrong forces.

Very often when we help others, when we become one with others' sorrow, we get a kind of joy. This is a very tricky thing. When somebody is sad or suffering, we try to help that person. But inwardly we may enjoy his suffering and have a glorified inner feeling that we have been of some help to him.

First we feel a little sorry; then we get joy because we feel superior. We think, "I am not suffering he is suffering. I am at the top of the tree and he is at the foot of the tree." This wrong idea very often enters into our mind. If we identify ourselves with someone who is sad and depressed, if we are just enjoying his sadness, we are not helping him at all.

Question: Does the Supreme make us depressed for a reason?

Sri Chinmoy: No! No, no, no! He has nothing to do with that. The Supreme does not want us to be depressed. Only we say to the Supreme that if He wants us to be depressed for a special reason, then we are ready. That is our surrender. But if we pray to the Supreme to keep us sad and miserable so that we will always think of Him, that is wrong. He is all Joy, all Love; so let us take His Joy and Love. He does not want us to have depression, but we cherish it.

Again, what we call depression at a particular moment, in His Eye may not be depression at all. Only we take it as such.

In the Pandava family, Arjuna's mother, Kunti, knew that Lord Krishna was a great spiritual Master. She knew that Sri Krishna was God Himself. So she used to pray to him to give her sorrow and suffering all the time so that she would think only of him. She believed that only if she lived in suffering would she be inspired to think of God. This idea is not good at all. Just to think of God we need not invoke extra suffering. This is a wrong approach to the truth.

The right way to approach the truth is through joy and light. The soul is full of divine joy, and from the soul joy wants to come forward and express itself through the vital. If the vital does not want to become one with the soul's joy, the vital consciously and deliberately resents this joy and stands in its way. At that time this unaspiring vital prefers suffering because it feels that by expressing suffering outwardly it draws the sympathy, affection and concern of the world. Despite the vital's suffering it is actually getting a subtle joy in a negative way.

Very often we think that if we become a victim to sadness, there will be somebody to console us. This is a wrong idea. God does not approve of this idea. Today we will be sad and our mother or father or friend or somebody will console us. This consolation and attention gives us joy, so tomorrow we will feel sad with the same idea that somebody will come and console us. But tomorrow perhaps others will be tired of consoling us and we will be disappointed. In God's creation there are some people who are always sad because they feel that when somebody comes to console them they will get real joy. They feel that the best way to get attention and affection is to tell the world that it does not care for them or that they are totally lost. But even if they sincerely feel that they are totally lost, the world is not going to take care of them forever if it is not the Will of God. God's Concern always runs in a positive direction.

Very often psychic joy wants to express itself directly, without the vital and even without the mind. But when it is about to express or it has expressed itself, the depression of the vital and the doubt of the mind enter into the joy of the heart and soul. Then the vital's depression and the mind's doubt immediately act like a devouring tiger. When they see this joy, they take it as a fruit and devour it immediately. After several times, the soul sees that its joy is being devoured by the mind and vital, and the soul becomes cautious. It does not want to express its joy quite so often. It waits for the vital to be purified and for the mind to be free from doubts.

Question: Is it really necessary to seek help when we are suffering from mental problems? Can't we just meditate by ourselves and find the answer?

Sri Chinmoy: Let us say that you are suffering from certain mental difficulties. You have surrendered to frustration and depression owing to countless problems in your life. You feel that there is light inside your heart, but you find it difficult to go deep within and bring that light into your mind. What you have to do is go to someone who can bring to the fore the light that you have within you. The light that you so desperately need is in your own house. But you have misplaced the key and you do not know how to open the door. So a friend of yours comes and helps you look for the key. After he finds it, he opens the door for you and then he goes away.

If you are ready to search by yourself for the key that you have lost, then you can try. But if you take the help of an expert friend, then you will have more confidence in finding the key. A spiritual teacher is an eternal friend who helps you in your search. He will advise you and offer light so that you can free yourself from your mental suffering.

Question: How can I prevent getting upset or depressed over small things, such as a car breakdown or a screaming child?

Sri Chinmoy: In the material world, whatever we handle, we should try to keep in perfect condition. If we are using an old car, naturally this may create problems. Even new cars sometimes give trouble. But we should always try to use a perfect instrument. Since we are trying to be perfect instruments of the Supreme, the things that we handle should also have perfection in them. Just as we cry and try for perfection of our own nature, whatever is our possession should also be perfect according to our standard. So the things that we are utilising as our instruments must be kept in perfect condition. But we have to know that in spite of the fact that something appears perfect, it often is not. And if it causes problems, does depression help us in any way? Never.

We must always be wise. A wise man will take an unfortunate happening as a challenge, an opportunity to face an unpleasant reality with a cheerful smile. A fool will curse his fate and will curse others. He will feel that this kind of misfortune only happens to him. A wise person will simply say, "Here I have another opportunity to conquer my anger or my depression." Every experience in life can be meaningful and beneficial if we accept it properly.

Now, when a child is screaming, what should we do? Immediately remember that his screaming is not stronger than your inner poise. Then try to bring forward your inner poise and let it drown out the screaming of the child. Every time you see something irritating or undivine, accept the challenge and conquer it. If you allow it to conquer you, you are bound to become upset or depressed.

Wait for God's Choice Hour.
Do not pressure Him.
Nothing good
Can ever come into existence,
Nothing good
Can ever be achieved
By pressure.

Question: What should we do if we are struggling and, at the same time, losing the quality of joy in our lives?

Sri Chinmoy: We have to know whether it is a real inner struggle. It is very easy for us to use the term "struggle." Again, "struggle" is a very complicated word. If a lazy person has to budge an inch, he calls it a struggle. If we have to get up early in the morning, or if we have to tell the truth, we say that it is a struggle. If we have to face reality for a fleeting second, if we have to work, it is all a struggle.

Each individual has to realise within himself what true struggle is. The real struggle for a sincere seeker is to conquer ignorance in his own life and in the world around him. But if he is sincerely struggling to conquer himself, to be the conqueror of his own life, then his very effort is bound to give him joy. If he is sincerely struggling against falsehood, inertia, darkness, imperfection, limitation and bondage, then he is bound to feel a kind of inner joy.

We have to know how hard we are trying to realise the Highest, how many minutes of our daily life we are consecrating to the Supreme in us, how much we are struggling to see the Light within us and within others. If we have this kind of struggle, then we are bound to feel that the divine qualities which we have and which everybody has are bound to increase. It is the divine qualities within us that are looming large and inspiring us to fight against teeming darkness and ignorance. So how can these divine qualities desert us when it is they who are asking us to fight? In really sincere spiritual struggle we are not going to lose our inner qualities. On the contrary, our inner qualities will increase in boundless measure.

Question: In one of your poems you say, "Hope lost... destruction close." What can one do if that person is losing hope? What can an aspirant do?

Sri Chinmoy: Why does a person lose hope? First of all, I wish to tell you why a person loses hope, not what he can do. Why does one lose hope? One loses hope because one feels that there is a certain period, a given time in which to achieve something. You have fixed the time, deciding that, for example, in two days you are going to achieve some specific thing. Now frequently in our hopes, we have inwardly fixed or recorded some particular time for the accomplishment of something. Outwardly we may say that in the near future, we hope to get something or to do something. But it is not entirely true. For if we go deep within ourselves, we see that our minds have already projected a particular date by which to finish something. Inside yourself, if you turn within, you will see that your mind has set the fifteenth of November, for example, as the date. Now when that date arrives, your outer mind may not know that this was the last date given or recorded in your inner mind's calendar. But on that day you will feel that everything has collapsed because you did not achieve and receive the hoped-for result. And when you don't see the result on that day, you feel miserable. You thought that hope was the instrument that would bring the result. On the given day, therefore, you lose hope; you lose the strength of hope even though your physical mind was not even aware of the day that was given by the inner mind. There you are lost. You lose hope.

What can you do to regain hope? Here we have to know that hope is not something weak. Very often our conception of hope is something very delicate; a sweet, smooth, soothing feeling which is a kind of balm to our outer minds. But this is not an adequate definition of hope. We have to know that hope is something very solid. It is something strong. It has seen the Truth, only it is unable to bring the Truth into its world. Hope is not something that is crying for the world beyond or crying for a truth which it has not seen. No. Hope has seen the Truth but it cannot and does not yet possess it.

So what can you do when you lose hope? If you know what it is, first of all, you will not lose it. If you know that hope is something that has already seen the Truth, which you are ultimately going to achieve, then you will get strength from this knowledge. The time has not come; hope has not yet been able to bring the Truth in front of you. The real time, which has been planned by God has not yet come.

Again, what can you do to get back your hope? Try to cast aside all expectations from your desiring mind. It is the desiring mind that feeds our outer hope. If we can be above the desiring mind, and remain all the time in the spontaneity of our heart, we will have a constant feeling of divine possession, of possessing the Truth. We shall know then that hope is the vision that sees the reality and finally becomes the reality itself in the Supreme's own Hour.

Our inner heart is always full and complete, requiring nothing. It is our outer mind, which feels that it needs something, wants something. Then hope comes into play. When you need something, hope begins to play its part, but when you need nothing, hope does not enter the picture, for it is not at all necessary.

I would like to point out that ordinary human hope can never be fulfilled because inside it there is no determination; there is no sincerity, there is no conscious willingness to accept the highest Truth. If, with our human hope, we want to achieve the Highest, the Ultimate, we will see that when the Highest is descending and descending, approaching our own human physical being, this human hope will be terrified and try to escape at the very moment that it sees the enormity of the reality that it was aspiring to possess.

Let us look at the fulfilment, in boundless measure, of our ordinary human hope. Hope expected something, say five dollars. When fulfilment came, it came as five million dollars; immediately this human hope was overjoyed. Immediately also it loses its inner poise. When spiritual receptivity is lacking, we always lose our inner balance and poise. But if you started with Divine Hope, where Truth is already seen in its highest aspect, it needs only to be embodied. Your hope is only to bring that Truth into manifestation. There you do not lose your inner balance. Then when hope's fulfilment comes into you, you do not become unbalanced because you knew about it. You knew what was bound to happen. You remain poised.

Your question was, "What can you do when you lose hope?" When you lose hope, you have to feel that the reality is bound to come to you precisely because you are in the world of aspiration. You are aspiring most sincerely, most devotedly, most uniquely. You are doing the right thing. Now if the Truth or the Fulfilment that your hope has envisioned has not yet been able to manifest, do not worry. It is only when you lose your aspiration that you can feel that you are lost. When I said in my aphorism, "Hope lost, destruction close," it is because the ordinary man will not aspire when there is no hope. It is hope that keeps him alive on earth. Hope plays a great part on earth. For example, some people say that they are doing disinterested work, and so on. Only aspirants and truly spiritual people really do this. Ninety-nine percent of human beings, in working, are only feeding their own human hopes and desires. That is why they are living, working, existing. Otherwise they would not budge an inch.

In a spiritual person, this aphorism "Hope lost, destruction close" does not apply. Where is destruction for a spiritual person? For him, there is no destruction. He acts only to fulfil God's Will. We tend to judge the fulfilment of God's Will in two ways, in the form of success or in the form of failure. But God Himself is above both success and failure. So if you want to become identified totally and inseparably with God's Will, then think neither of success nor of failure. Think only of pleasing the Supreme. According to our human eyes, the fulfilment of hope is success. But according to our divine vision, the fulfilment of God's Will is far above and infinitely higher than the achievement of failure or success.

If you remain with your burning aspiration, you are constantly identified with God's Will. And when you are one with God's Will, this earthly hope has no value. It will be impossible for earthly hope to knock at your door of aspiration because your divine hope is already self-sufficient. It is already one with God's Will. In God's Will there is everything, the Vision and the Reality. If the Reality is success, well and good. It is the fulfilment of God's Will, which is of paramount importance, not success or failure. Fulfilment is always beyond results. We see the results best and we derive the utmost benefit from the results only when we are one with God's Will unreservedly. When we are identified with His Will unreservedly, we know that we are fulfilled.

What can you do when you lose hope? Only feel the necessity of burning the flame of your aspiration more brightly and more intensely. Then you get the Highest. Hope you don't need. For an ordinary person, (not you) but an unaspiring person – when he loses hope, it is destruction, because he won't make any move forward. For him life becomes a stagnant pool. Self-destruction starts when there is no forward movement. But not you. You have aspiration. You will get everything.

Taking on the world

To have absolute inner peace
In the face of life's outer agitation
Is the meaning of divine poise.

Question: There is a lot of sickness and sadness in the world. What is the best way to seek spiritual healing?

Sri Chinmoy: The best way to seek spiritual healing is to offer gratitude every day for a fleeting second to the Supreme Healer. When we offer gratitude to Him for what we have or for what we are right now, then our heart of aspiration and dedication expands. That means that our receptivity increases. When receptivity increases, God's Light, which is all healing, can enter into us in abundant measure. It is in the heart of gratitude that God's Light can permanently abide.

Illness is all around. How can we cure it? We can cure it only through our gratitude-heart. We have to offer our gratitude to the Absolute Supreme that He has given us the sincere inner cry to cure humanity's suffering. There are many who do not care to cure illness either within themselves or within the world. There are many millions and billions of people on earth, but how many are crying to cure the sufferings and ills of mankind? Very few. But just because we are seekers, we are crying and trying to cure the age-old illnesses and sufferings of mankind. Now, who has given us this good will, this aspiration, this inner cry? God Himself. So it is our bounden duty to offer Him our gratitude. There are many around us – our friends. relatives, neighbours, acquaintances – who do not pray to God or meditate on God. But we do. And who has given us this capacity? God Himself. So, if at every moment we can offer our gratitude to God, then the receptivity of our heart increases.

And inside our receptivity is all strength, all light, all power to cure the sufferings of mankind.

Question: When something in the world bothers me, I lose all my sincerity and become depressed.

Sri Chinmoy: You have to know that there is a great difference between sincerity and stupidity. If somebody has told a lie, you must try to illumine that person. If a mistake has been made by somebody, you must try to rectify that mistake inwardly or outwardly by offering your good will. In your own case, stupidity comes into the picture. If you have done something wrong, you feel that by increasing your guilt you will solve the problem. But this is not the right approach. Always think of the goal, which is perfection. You have to bring perfection into the picture.

If something wrong has been done, either by you or by somebody else, at that time you have to offer the result immediately to the Supreme. You have to say, "I was helpless, he was helpless. We were attacked by wrong forces. We know that we were attacked and we want to offer our mistake to you." Again, you have to be conscious and wise. Once you discover that you are doing something wrong, you have to stop doing that thing.

Depression is not the answer. When you run a race, if you are disqualified, what will you do? You will wait for another day and then again try to reach the goal. Just because you have had an unfortunate experience, if you stop competing in the race, you will never reach the goal. A sad experience must not be the ultimate experience. Take it as a passing cloud. You will definitely come out of this ignorance-cloud.

Depression is dangerous.
Depression is self-destructive.
Depression is the real failure
In our spiritual life.

Question: When I read the newspapers and see all the suffering and violence in the world, it upsets me.

Sri Chinmoy: If you are disturbed by reading newspapers, then why do you read newspapers? If there are thorns lying right in front of you, will you walk on the thorns and then feel miserable because your feet hurt? This is stupidity. If you know that the newspaper is full of undivine forces on every page, which is true, then why do you read it? In the spiritual life, if you want to make the fastest progress, you should always read the things that will inspire you and lead you towards your goal.

There are people who read newspapers and they are not affected. I read *The New York Times* occasionally. I am not affected because I see it as an experience. I know that whatever has happened has been recorded in the cosmos, in the universe. Of course, I sympathise. While I am reading, I sympathise with the sufferer. But if I cherish or harbour that person's suffering, then my meditation will be useless. So when I meditate I don't think of how someone has shot someone else; I do not allow any force like this to enter.

You have to know how much capacity you have. You have to accept and reject the world according to your capacity. If you do not have the capacity to accept the experience as an experience, then it is not necessary to read the newspaper at all. Things that stand in the way of your inner life must be discarded like a dirty, filthy rag. You should constantly deal only with the things that inspire you. If the newspaper stands as an obstacle in your way, if it destroys your inner poise, which is your real wealth, then you don't have to read it. But just because you see something in front of you, out of curiosity you want to touch it. If you see a flame and touch it out of curiosity, naturally you will be burnt.

The best way to seek spiritual healing is to offer gratitude every day for a fleeting second to the Supreme Healer.

Question: From the point of view of a lot of people, the world is a very cruel and negative place and their consciousness is not in a position to absorb the negativity. What can you say, or what service can we perform ("we" in the largest sense of the word) to help with that situation?

Sri Chinmoy: I fully agree with you. What we should do is to cultivate more soulful patience. Right now the world is far from perfection. It is an almost half-animal world that we are living in. We are constantly quarrelling and fighting. But again, there is an inner cry in us to do something, to become something, to grow into something that will give us abiding satisfaction. This inner cry is something that wants to transcend what we have now and what we are now. But perfection does not come into existence overnight. It takes time.

What you need, what I need, what others need, is one thing: soulful patience. We have to know that patience is not something weak. If we are patient, it does not mean that we are forced to surrender to the hard reality of life. No, it is inner wisdom. Our inner wisdom needs patience, a length of time. It is like a seed. As soon as we see a seed, we expect the seed to grow into a plant and become a tree, a huge banyan tree. But the seed takes time to germinate and gradually become a plant and then a tree. If we have the vision of our patience, then one day we will see that truth will manifest and grow into Reality. So what the entire world needs is soulful patience. Then the truth can grow in its own way.

Caring for others

Question: How can we help someone who is very upset about something?

Sri Chinmoy: When somebody is upset, first try to invoke peace into that person's system or into yourself as quickly as possible. It may be extremely difficult to bring peace into him at that moment because that person is angry and upset. At that time he does not want to take the medicine he needs, which is peace.

But you yourself have, let us say, limited peace. You have to invoke the Supreme to increase your peace-power – whatever peace you have within you – even if it is only the smallest quantity. I always say that if you have a little life-energy, then only will the doctor give you an injection. Otherwise, if you are already dead, the doctor is not going to give you an injection to increase your life-energy.

You definitely have a little peace – that is why you are able to observe that the other person is so upset. Right away invoke a very large amount of peace to descend into your entire being. You will try to become the ocean of peace. Then, like a mirror, just go and stand in front of that person. His anger will be nothing in comparison to the peace which you have invoked.

That is one way. Another way is to make yourself feel that you are the culprit, even though you are not. Somebody else has caused the person to be upset; you are not the culprit at all. But you have to make yourself feel most sincerely that you are the one who has offended the person in question. Make yourself feel absolutely helpless and guilty. Feel that you are the guilty party, even though you have done nothing wrong. Then, inside you, on the strength of your sympathetic oneness, invoke the consciousness of the actual culprit. The real culprit's undivine consciousness at that time you are borrowing for a few seconds. Then, once you become the culprit, surrender to the victim who is now so mad and furious. Become absolutely helpless. Feel miserable that you have caused the person to become so upset.

When you act like a helpless human being, all the victim's anger and frustration will go away. She will say, "All right, she is an object of pity. She has done something wrong. Now she fully realises it, so I have to forgive her."

This is a very, very clever way of calming someone who is extremely upset. Many times it happens in an affectionate family. I have seen it, especially in India. The culprit is somewhere else, but an affectionate mother or sister or brother makes themself feel that they are the real culprit. They are not actually the culprit, but by feeling this way, they bring into themselves the consciousness of the actual culprit. Then the victim sees the remorse. When he sees that the culprit has real remorse, real sadness, he feels that he is now on a higher level and that it is up to him to forgive.

This second way is on a very practical level. On the spiritual level, you can try to invoke peace into the system of the person who is mad and furious – which is really difficult – or to bring more peace into your own

system. If the person is facing an ocean of peace, he will see that his anger is nothing in comparison to that peace.

Question: If a friend is suffering from a negative emotion, from hostility or anger, how can you help that person?

Sri Chinmoy: First you have to see how much capacity you have. To help your friend, you can go only so far. You may be near the shore, and your friend may also be very near the shore. Let us say that you have given your hand and you are about to pull your friend from the sea of ignorance. You have to know if you have the capacity to lift your friend and bring him to the shore, or if your friend will take you into the water. You have to be careful. You have to see how much strength you have. Your friend desperately needs your help, but will you succeed, or will he pull you into the water?

When a friend suffers, in your prayers you have to say to the Supreme, "If it is Your Will, then do give me the capacity to be of service to You inside my friend. If it is not Your Will, then please, please, I do not want to be involved. I shall only offer my goodwill. If it is Your Will, I will become involved because I know I will be protected. But if it is not Your Will, then I am only using my self-styled concern and compassion." If your friend is suffering from problems – depression, frustration, emotional problems and so on – the best thing is to pray to the Supreme and get an inner message about what you should do at that point. From your prayers you will get inner guidance, and this inner guidance will tell you what to do. Then whatever help you are supposed to give to that particular person you will be able to give.

Question: Could my own inner joy help the rest of my family, like my husband?

Sri Chinmoy: It is quite possible. Everything is divinely or undivinely contagious. Not only does the sadness or depression of others affect us, but their happiness also can easily enter into us. It is not only possible; it is inevitable. If you stay with a bad person, his badness is contagious.

If you stay with a good person, his goodness is also contagious. Why do birds of a feather flock together? Because consciously they help each other. Your husband does not follow the spiritual life, but your very presence will give him joy in a very small measure. If you are happy, then eventually he also can become happy. But if he tries and cries, then he will have happiness sooner.

Question: How can we know if we are being justifiably strict with ourselves or unnecessarily self-critical in a negative way?

Sri Chinmoy: If we sincerely aspire, inside our aspiration there will be justice-light. If you have burning aspiration, inside your aspiration there will be light, and according to that light you will judge yourself in a just manner. The light will illumine the confusion of the mind that is too self-critical or the mind that is saying that you can take a little more leisure or pleasure. The intensity of your aspiration is bound to tell you whether you are too self-critical, too lenient or too indulgent. Aspiration has light in it, so the light will show you whether this place is dark, or full of confusion, or full of mental hallucination. Let us say that one side is hallucination, and the other side is confusion. If you bring a flashlight, then if you are criticising yourself and you want to be more strict with yourself, the light will say, "No, it is not necessary." Again, if you are being too self-indulgent, the light will say, "You have to be more strict."

There are very few people who are self–critical. Sometimes pride enters into self-critical people. They say, "Oh, I am the only one who wants to be perfect." Self-critical people think that they are the only ones who are longing for perfect perfection. They feel that only they will attain perfect perfection, and others will not. Of course, that idea may not come to their conscious mind.

By criticising myself, I cannot come to the light. By criticising myself, I only weaken myself, because I am deliberately giving up the positive aspect of life. If I feel that I am not perfect, or I have not come up to a certain point, then let me become perfect. If I feel that today I cannot give myself a hundred out of a hundred, if I can only give myself 60, still

I must not criticise myself. I should only say, "Today I have given myself 60. Tomorrow let me see if I can give myself 70." By criticising myself because I have got a mark of 60 today when I expected to get 80 or 90, I lose my mental poise, and then I ruin my possibilities.

If you have given a low mark to yourself, and you feel that you have been impartial and given a just mark, do not criticise yourself. If you criticise yourself, if you say, "How can I get only 50?" you are only weakening yourself. Instead, you should say, "I have given myself a low mark. Now let me have more determination. Instead of criticising myself, let me take the positive point of view. Let me get a higher mark on the strength of my determination."

Question: Will people who are depressed ever realise God?

Sri Chinmoy: They will, but they will undoubtedly be the last group to realise God unless they conquer their depression. And when they reach God, God will not be proud of them. Out of Compassion God will allow them to drink His Nectar, but God will be pleased and will feed with pride only those who are constantly marching forward and not looking backward. God will tolerate doubt and depression, but only those who are truly cheerful inwardly and outwardly will have everything open to them.

God is Light, and those who suffer from depression are not accepting God's Light. If they think that by being depressed, they will get more Compassion from God or from their Guru, they are mistaken. God and the Guru may show them infinite Compassion, but it will not be wholehearted Compassion. God and the Guru *will* know that they are being exploited by the aspirant's constant demands for Compassion.

If they say that God does not love them enough, it is all their negative imagination and self-justification. Who loves His children more than the Father? Fortunately for them, God's Compassion is infinite. But although those who are depressed will eventually realise God also, the path of cheerfulness is infinitely swifter.

The power of poise

If we have inner poise,
Then in each and every field
We can achieve tremendous success.

Question: How can we remain peaceful when we're trying to accomplish something powerful?

Sri Chinmoy: You have to know where power actually lies. If you feel that power lies only in running and jumping and struggling, then you are mistaken. The real power lies in inmost silence. So if you want to know how you can remain peaceful while doing something powerful, then I wish to say that you have to understand the meaning of the word 'powerful.' Power here means the poise of one's inner being, one's soul. If you have a free access to your inner being, to your soul, then automatically your outer action will be peaceful. You do not have to raise your hands and show off your outer capacity. No! Here there is no dramatic performance. If you are acquainted with what you inwardly have and inwardly are, if you have free access to your inner being, then automatically you taste the bliss of silence. And if you taste the bliss of silence, in your outer action you will all the time be peaceful.

So, powerful action is the result of inner poise. This powerful action is not vital action or something that is seen in the movement itself. No, it is only in the silent equanimity, in the very heart of silence, that you get this power. If you feel this power and enter into it, then everything is peaceful around you.

You cannot enjoy in your outer life
The lion-roar
If you do not have in your inner life
The lion-poise.

Question: Can I develop more inner poise through prayer?

Sri Chinmoy: Prayer can give you everything. If you don't have poise, your prayer is bound to give you poise. But I wish to say that everybody comes into the world with some inner poise. The soul has all the divine qualities in seed form. The soul is a portion of divinity, so naturally everything will be there. But poise can be in the physical in an absolutely negligible quantity. If you try, you can develop an ocean of poise from one drop. Even if you think that you don't have a drop of poise, no harm. The Supreme will give you abundant poise just because you are praying. Then, a time will come when your whole being will be flooded with inner poise. You are praying and praying and your inner being is storing up your poise, keeping it secret. Then one day you will see that you are all poise, boundless poise.

Question: How can we achieve self-poise?

Sri Chinmoy: We can achieve self-poise by realising the fact that the world does not belong to us; it belongs only to God.

Question: If something wrong happens or if I miss some good opportunity, I just pray for surrender, but I do not achieve it.

Sri Chinmoy: You have to feel that you are in a running race. When it is over, you will offer the result to the Supreme. But in your case, when you have lost or done poorly, you suffer and you curse the Supreme. Right before the action takes place, it is easy to offer the action to the Supreme. But afterwards, you blame Him to whom you offered your most soulful surrender.

141

Again, when we win the race, when the result is most satisfactory, very often the result does not go to the Supreme; it goes to our pride and vanity. We say, "Because of my personal effort, I have achieved this victory. I have worked very hard. That is why I deserve it." Outwardly we say that the result must go to the Supreme, but inwardly we don't offer it.

We have to keep the attitude of surrender and it has to be a living attitude in our life, whether we win or lose. We may fail hundreds of times, but we will keep offering our failure to the Supreme. We shall offer the result either in the form of failure or success with the same cheerfulness. It is a very difficult task and a long process; but this is the only way we can be really happy.

> *The inner cheerfulness*
> *Is*
> *The outer depression-antidote.*

Question: What changes do we have to make when we have to work and eat with other persons who do not feel what we feel? Sometimes I have harsh reactions in my relations with the world.

Sri Chinmoy: It is true that you are superior to a street urchin because you are consciously praying to God and an ordinary person in the street is not thinking of God, is not praying to God, is not concentrating or meditating on God. In that way, naturally you are superior. But if you yourself consciously cherish the idea that you are a superior individual, then naturally you create a barrier between your existence and the existence of the people around you.

Let us use an analogy. The mother is naturally superior to the child. But the mother does not consciously feel, twenty-four hours a day, that she is superior. What she feels is that she is absolutely one with the child. Hers is a feeling of oneness and not a feeling of superiority. It is we who say that the Mother has more knowledge, wisdom, more capacity, than the child. But if the mother consciously harbours the idea that she is superior to her child, then she won't be able to show affection or concern or be able to do anything for the child.

So if you consider the world around you and feel that you are superior because they are acting in an animal way, you won't be able to become one with them and enter into them. It is we, the witnesses, who will make the comparison, that you are superior to others who are not aspiring, who are still sleeping.

How can we mix with people who are not aspiring, who are destructive in their relationship with us? You lose your patience and you lose your temper, it is true.

Every day, I am sure, you try to meditate. You not only try, you do meditate every day. Now when you go out, try to feel that your wallet is your spiritual bank. Early in the morning you meditated for five minutes and you gathered Peace, Light, Bliss and Power, etc. This all are your money, your wealth. Just like nickels, dimes and dollar bills, you are putting all this money into your wallet. This is inner wealth, however. In the morning you meditated and you collected the money, this spiritual wealth, which you are putting into your wallet.

In your outer life, the moment you are displeased with someone, and you are about to fly into a rage, always when you are about to burst into fury, immediately try to open your inner wallet where you have kept the inner peace. These are the pennies, nickels, dimes, quarters and bills that you have saved. If you can use your inner wealth, which is inside your wallet, then you will not be attacked by the wrong forces; at the same time, the peace and poise that you get from your inner wealth will prevent you from attacking them with your human power. What you will do while they are attacking you is to show your money, your light, bliss, peace, joy, etc. Just open your inner wallet and show them the solid protection that you have. They will not be able to enter into your inner sanctum when you have placed right in front of you a solid wall, which is composed of your inner wealth.

Every day when you meditate, try to feel that the result of your meditation will be in the form of spiritual currency and this currency you are putting into your wallet for later use. Then you will see that the rest of the world will not be able to torture you. At the same time, you will have no occasion to attack them.

Cultivating cheerfulness

My heart's cheerfulness-sunshine
Has at last illumined
My mind's despair-night.

Question: What is the best way to become cheerful and dynamic?

Sri Chinmoy: Every day, every hour, every minute, consciously try to convince your mind that you are seven years old. Then imagine what you were doing at the age of seven. Perhaps your mother was doing this or that with you, or your father was taking you here and there. At that time you did everything with such dynamism and cheerfulness. Perhaps your parents were getting someone to teach you to ride a horse and play the flute in the hope that one day you would become a great rider or musician. Even if these things did not happen on the physical plane, imagine that you were doing these things, and imagine how happy you were. If you can bring back to your conscious mind the enthusiasm and eagerness that you felt when you were seven, then easily you can be dynamic and cheerful.

> *There is only one*
> *Secret and sacred chain*
> *That links man and God,*
> *And that chain is*
> *Man's cheerfulness-heart.*

Cheerfulness is not excitement. Cheerfulness is my inner poise, and it is also God's complete Faith in me. Another name of my inner poise is God's unreserved Confidence in me.

> *Nothing can equal cheerfulness-treasure.*
> *This treasure is infinitely greater*
> *Than an emperor's wealth.*
> *Therefore, establish, increase*
> *And continually multiply*
> *Your cheerfulness-treasure.*

Question: How can I be more thankful to God?

Sri Chinmoy: Just by thinking of gratitude, we cannot become grateful. Our gratitude is like a magnet that pulls God's Compassion down to us. But before our gratitude begins to operate, first God has to pull us toward Him. Once God has started to pull us up, then our gratitude begins to grow and we can pull Him down into us.

There is a special way for a seeker to offer thanks or gratitude to God. It is through cheerfulness, constant cheerfulness. A seeker cannot allow depression to enter into his life of aspiration at any time. He always has to be happy in order to be truly grateful. But if his happiness comes from wallowing in the pleasures of ignorance, that is not the right kind of happiness. Real happiness is something within us which constantly makes us feel that we are expanding our consciousness and wholeheartedly embracing the entire world.

Today is St. Patrick's Day. In Ireland people commemorate this saint with sports, dancing, singing, drinking and being as happy as they can. Ordinary human happiness is found in this kind of fun and enjoyment. But the seeker within us will have a different type of happiness. On St. Patrick's Day green is worn. Spiritually, green signifies new hope and new satisfaction. For the seeker, happiness is a feeling of new hope, new life, new dawn, new promise, new achievement. These feelings the seeker has to nourish and treasure within himself. If the seeker in us cherishes these divine qualities, automatically our thankfulness to God will grow; our gratitude-flower will blossom and we will be able to offer it at the Feet of the Lord Supreme.

In spiritual happiness, in the happiness that comes from self-giving and aspiration, gratitude looms large. When we have inner happiness, we don't have to search for gratitude here and there. In our devoted cheerfulness, in our soulful cheerfulness, we are bound to discover constantly-increasing gratitude to the Supreme.

God never likes our sad loneliness.
He likes our heart's and mind's
Cheerfulness
More than anything else.

5

Healthy Sleep

Sleep
Is not rest.
Sleep
Is energy-gathering wisdom.

How to get more rest while sleeping

Question: What is the best position to sleep in?

Sri Chinmoy: Some people do not know how to sleep properly. They sleep flat on their chest, which is an absurd way of sleeping. At that time the *Ida, Pingala* and *Sushumna* cords cannot function at all. Always you have to face the light and allow the light to enter at the heart centre. When you are sleeping on your back or on your side, you are seeing some light, whereas when you sleep on your chest, light is immediately obstructed. So the best way to sleep is on your side or on your back. Never lie facing down, and do not cross your arms or hands on your chest when you sleep.

Question: Is insomnia a blessing or a curse?

Sri Chinmoy: For an ordinary person insomnia is really a curse. He needs sleep. Insomnia will tell upon his health and he won't be able to function properly in the world-scene. But for a spiritual seeker who has learned the art of meditation, if he does not get much sleep or does not want to sleep because he wants to meditate more at night, this is good. If he can meditate well and, at the same time, if his health is not affected, then if he wants to meditate three or four hours a night, it is wonderful.

Some people are very sincere and they want to meditate for hours and hours. During the day they have the capacity to meditate for four or five hours, and at night also they want to meditate. They try their best, but after a while they fall asleep. But if nature does not give them sleep and if this does not in any way disturb their health, it is a real blessing. Then they don't have to fight against sleep during their meditation; they don't have to think of conquering sleep. In their case, sleep is kind to them if it does not visit them.

In India there is a special god named *Shani*. You call him Saturn. He is the god of renunciation. Ordinary people are afraid of him and pray to him to bless them by staying away from them. Other gods people invoke to come and bless them, but to *Shani* they say, "Please grant us the blessing of not coming to us. If you ignore us, that is the best blessing." Similarly, the seeker will consider it a real blessing if sleep does not come to him. The few hours that he can meditate at night will add to his meditation during the day. And the more he can meditate soulfully and devotedly without his body being adversely affected, the better it is. But for the non-seeker who is not meant for spiritual life right now, if he does not get enough sleep, it is a curse. Something will go wrong in his physical body, or something may already be amiss.

Question: If we are tired or sick, should we sleep more?

Sri Chinmoy: If we are very tired or sick we should sleep according to our body's necessity, but not according to our body's demands; for the body, being unconscious and ignorant, may demand sleep more than its due.

Question: Sometimes it seems a shame that we spend one third of our lives in sleep.

Sri Chinmoy: Ask your sincerity. If you sincerely need God then you don't have to spend that many hours in sleep. Sincerity has to answer this question: How desperately do you need God? Imagine that somebody is pressing your head under water. You are dying for a breath, your whole being cries only for air. If you need God as much as you would need air if you were in this situation, if God's existence comes first and foremost in your life, and if you feel that you can exist without air, water, food or anybody, but not without God, then you don't have to sleep so many hours. Sincerity is the answer. Your sincerity will solve the problem.

Question: Is it true that you actually become more tired if you sleep longer than five or six hours?

Sri Chinmoy: It is not a question of five or six hours, but if you really sleep more than your body's necessity, then a disproportionate amount of lethargy attacks your body. Because of this merciless attack, you feel more tired.

Sleep and spiritual seekers

Question: How much sleep is necessary for a spiritual seeker?

Sri Chinmoy: It entirely depends on how much will-power you have that can create receptivity in the body. If your will-power can create receptivity in the physical consciousness, then only one or two hours, or even less, is necessary. If you can't create receptivity, then it is always advisable to take rest. Otherwise, the consciousness does not function properly. If the consciousness does not function, then we are worse than animals. It not only does not function; what is worse, it becomes destructive. Destruction takes place in the form of negative feelings towards everything, towards your own existence. If you cherish negative feelings, that is real death.

Question: When I go to sleep at night I feel a pressure to remain in meditation longer, and when I sleep my dreams tell me to wake up and meditate. If I ignore them, the next dream says that my higher self is very unhappy.

Sri Chinmoy: No matter what your dreams say, in your particular case you need a minimum of seven hours of sleep in order for your body and mind to get enough rest. If you let your dreams make you feel that when you are sleeping you are wasting your precious time, then when you are meditating, the light of your inner voice will tell you that your health is suffering because you are not taking the necessary rest. At the present stage of your spiritual evolution you need seven hours of sleep. But the hostile forces like to create problems for us. According to them, no matter what we do, we are always doing something wrong. You have to be firm about this. You must tell them, "What I am doing is right for me and I don't want to hear anything else." If you want to meditate more, you will have to begin your meditation earlier, rather than continuing it later and taking the time away from your necessary rest.

Sleep, sleep, O Beauty's peace,
Sleep within me.
I shall give you a song from Eternity's Songbook.
Sleep, sleep within me.

Question: In one of your books you said that four hours of sleep is all you need if you are meditating. Would you speak about this? I would love to have more time.

Sri Chinmoy: Everything can be developed, like muscle-power. When you exercise your physical muscles, they become stronger. Similarly, if you pray and meditate, you can get a kind of inner power. Gradually you can increase the length of your meditation. Then meditation itself will give you the power to remain awake. Meditation will strengthen the nerves. We have 86,000 subtle nerves. When the subtle nerves become strong, you do not need seven or eight hours of sleep. But right now, for my disciples, seven hours is good.

Gradually, gradually you can try to bring it down. I always say, if you take coffee ten times a day, then bring it down to nine times, eight times, seven times and so on. In exactly the same way, you can try to reduce the amount you sleep. From seven hours, if you want to suddenly bring it down to four hours, you may perhaps do it for two days. Then, on the third day, you will not be able to get up. You will say, "I have meditated for so many days. Let me take rest." Everything has to be done very, very slowly, regularly and systematically. If you have been accustomed to sleeping for seven hours, then please try to sleep only fifteen minutes less. Try to continue with six hours and forty-five minutes for a few weeks or a few months. In this way it will be possible for you to sleep less. There is no short cut. From seven hours if you try to bring it down to four or three, it will tell upon your health. But if you do it slowly, regularly and systematically, it is not only quite possible but inevitable.

The number of hours that you sleep is not the important thing, but rather how well you sleep. If you find that it is difficult to get up in the morning, you have to know that during eight hours of sleep perhaps you have not had even one hour of good sleep. There is a kind of sleep called yogic sleep. In one second of yogic sleep we can get the equivalent of fifteen minutes or a half hour of ordinary rest.

Now, how can you get that kind of rest? Early in the morning when you find it difficult to get up, try to feel that your entire body, from head to foot, represents a sea of peace. Feel that you have become peace itself, that you embody peace within and without. Try to feel your physical frame consciously, but at the same time feel that you are an infinite expanse of peace. When you can consciously feel this expanse of peace, you will see that your physical body, flesh, blood and bones, has totally merged and disappeared into that sea of peace.

Peace can act like dynamic strength. You feel that when the body is active and moving to and fro, you have strength; but real strength exists in inner peace, not in outer action. When you possess peace in infinite measure, you possess the source of ordinary dynamic energy. If you call upon dynamic energy, which is inside you in the form of peace, then you can get up easily.

Also, when you go to bed, just try to feel that you are going to sleep for twenty-four hours. Then, even though the clock will say that you have slept only three or four hours, your very first thought as soon as you wake up should be that you have slept for twenty-four hours. The mind can convince the outer consciousness, and immediately you will believe it. This is not self-deception; it is proper use of the conscious mind. The figure twenty-four has enormous strength. It immediately gives us a sense of comfort, relief, pleasure, fulfilment.

Overcoming fatigue

Question: If we do not drink coffee or tea, what can we do if we start feeling drowsy while driving late at night?

Sri Chinmoy: You say that sometimes you feel drowsy while driving. Now, why should coffee or tea have to come to your rescue? There are spiritual methods, which have infinitely more power than coffee or tea, that can help you at that time. If you are tired while driving, stop your car and breathe in deeply a few times. Do the alternate nostril breathing. This will give you immediate energy. Then, with the power of your concentration, try consciously to breathe in divine energy. When you breathe in, try to feel that you are breathing in not only through your nose, but also through your eyes, ears, forehead, head, shoulders. Feel that energy is coming from all quarters and entering into you from various doors. If you are conscious of this stream of energy entering into you, naturally you will not be sleepy. When you begin meditating well, you are drawing in energy consciously or unconsciously. Naturally, the more energy you can draw into you, the higher your meditation will be. And where does this energy come from? It comes from the Universal Consciousness.

Another thing you can do when you are tired is repeat the name of the Supreme or your Guru very rapidly. If you do so, immediately their names will enter into your own inner consciousness, and you will get boundless energy.

Exercise

Overcoming fatigue

Try to invoke the Power aspect of the Supreme. At that time, do not invoke Peace or Light. Try to bring forward divine Power from within or bring down the Power from above. Immediately, in five minutes' time, you will feel energised. If you invoke dynamic power within yourself, you will see that your whole body will become energised with divine Power.

Try to repeat the name of the Supreme as fast as possible. It is not a race, but see how many times you can repeat "Supreme" with each breath. Then, when you feel the power inside the repetition of this name, your whole being will be inundated with divine energy and you are bound to feel a new flow of life and energy. If you repeat "Supreme" that way for five minutes, you will not fall asleep. Your utterance will enter into you as energy.

Try to feel inside you a dynamic and progressive movement, but not an aggressive one. This movement undoubtedly will take you to your destination. If there is a dynamic and progressive movement, then you cannot fall asleep. Inside you, feel that the train is running, running towards the destination; feel that you yourself are this very train. Then you cannot fall asleep.

Sleep and spiritual development

Question: Is it possible to make progress while you are asleep?

Sri Chinmoy: In ordinary sleep you are tired, exhausted. But if you can stay in Yogic sleep, that is not ordinary sleep. It is soundless sleep. But "soundless" is a very mild word. In that sleep, you do not have any dream, you do not have any desire, you do not have any conflict with the finite. Only you remain in the infinite. Your consciousness stays in Infinity and Eternity. So in this kind of sleep, you do make the fastest progress. It is not sleep but conscious aspiration that will help you. Just by sleeping many hours a day, if you feel that you will get realisation, then you are sadly mistaken.

Question: Is there some way that we can use the time when we are sleeping to further our progress, so that we can carry our day's consciousness through the night with us?

Sri Chinmoy: When you sleep, you sometimes get all kinds of vital dreams from the vital world, just rubbish. Why do you get these? Because your sleep is not sound, because you have not entered into the sleep world fully. When you go to bed, you actually sleep perhaps only three hours a night. The rest of the time you remain asleep just because it is not time for you to get up. What makes you sleep that long? It is your inertia, your body-consciousness. Your body-consciousness may say that if you sleep for ten hours, then the next day you will be able to work very hard and solve all your problems. But sleep cannot overcome your problems and difficulties. It is only conscious aspiration that will clear your life of problems. If you sleep for eight, nine, ten hours, you may only forget your problems. But then the following morning you will see that they are coming back much more vehemently.

If we take night as something for comfort, for peaceful rest, then night will give us lethargic comfort and not fulfilling rest. Fulfilling rest comes as a result of the day's labour, from spiritual effort, spiritual awakening. During the day we have meditated, we have worked very hard. Now, the result of this effort can be used during the night. If we try to feel the result of day during the night, then we shall see that day has actually entered into night. Otherwise, day and night will be like two separate beings. Day has played its role by seven o'clock, and night starts. We have played with one being, and now we have to play with the other.

For spiritual people there is no night. Night, for us, means ignorance, unconsciousness, inconscience. For spiritual people all is consciousness, all is conscience. If we take to the spiritual life, we have to remain awake and alert at every moment. How? Only by lengthening the conscious part of our life, which is day. When we meditate during the day, we are energised. So let us continue this dynamic feeling even into the night. Let us take night as something energising and fulfilling, as the lengthening of day.

After we have slept for an hour or two, if we wake up and feel that just for a few seconds we are conscious but not meditating, the best thing is immediately to get up and meditate for five, ten or fifteen minutes. At that time, we have to try to feel that the day has entered into our consciousness, that our day has already begun. Now what does this mean? It means our consciousness is fully alert; it is awakened and vigilant and doesn't want to sleep. The body may sleep, but the consciousness is already fully awakened and meditating on our behalf. If we feel that we are lethargic and heavy, that our mind is not functioning, we should pay no attention to this thought. If we feel that if we get up, then the next day we won't be able to work, this is wrong. No, we will be able to work. We must always try to feel that night can be transformed into day through our awakened consciousness.

In some spiritual communities at three o'clock or three-thirty all the members have to get up to meditate together. When the Ramakrishna

Math was first established, it was Vivekananda's order that everybody had to get up at three-thirty to meditate, no matter how high his rank. If any individuals didn't get up then, those who were awake were allowed to sprinkle unbearably cold water on them. Once the president of the Math, Rakhal (Brahmananda), was not feeling well, and he could not or did not want to get up. Somebody told Vivekananda that Rakhal didn't want to get up. Vivekananda said, "The same rule applies to him. You go and pull him out of the bed." Rakhal got very mad, and he wanted to leave the Math. He said, "I am president and this young boy, a disciple of mine, comes and insults me. You know I am sick; otherwise I wouldn't violate your rule. I am leaving. I don't want to stay here."

But Vivekananda was very clever. He said, "Whose place is this? Ramakrishna never called me his son; he always used to call you his son. Now, the father's property belongs to the son. This is your place, your Math. Here is your father's mission, your father's realisation. You have to stay; I shall go away." Brahmananda didn't want Vivekananda to go, so the matter was settled. This story shows how Vivekananda made it a hard and fast rule that everybody had to get up early in the morning, no matter how high the position. And it did help; it did help.

There is a kind of sleep called yogic sleep.
In one second of yogic sleep we can get
the equivalent of fifteen minutes or a half
hour of ordinary rest.

Question: How can we stay conscious when we're sleeping?

Sri Chinmoy: In your case, since you only meditate a half hour or an hour a day, it is not possible. If one wants to be fully alert during sleep and not disturbed by vital, emotional forces or wrong movements, then one has to meditate at least six and a half hours daily. And in that meditation one cannot all the time be looking at the clock to see how many hours have gone by. One may not watch the time, but he must know that he is meditating at least six hours daily. If one can meditate consciously for six or seven hours – and not only for a day or two, but for a few months, perhaps even a few years – then only can one be fully conscious during sleep. At that time he will be able to know which plane his soul is moving in during sleep. Like a bird, the soul flies from this plane to that plane during sleep, and one can be fully conscious of this movement if he meditates.

But I do not advise one who has plenty of work to do in his office or at school to meditate six or seven hours a day. First of all, if the vital is not pure, it will immediately create problems greater than the achievement in meditation. The person will lose his mental balance and will have to go to a mental asylum. Gradually one can work up to six hours a day. It is like exercising the body; every day you take exercise and gradually you develop your muscles. Then you feel strong and others feel you are strong. Similarly, you have to start with fifteen minutes or half an hour of meditation and gradually increase it. In the spiritual world, you cannot push or pull or do things by force. Slowly and steadily you run towards the Goal. At each step you have to be confident of what you are doing. If you have been meditating for half an hour, you can try to meditate for forty-five minutes or an hour, but from half an hour please do not jump to six and a half hours.

If you cannot meditate for six hours, which you cannot and must not try right now, before you go to bed I wish you to breathe purity into your system consciously for five minutes. During the day, many wrong things have taken place. Impurity, ugliness and many other undivine forces

have entered into your physical body. But if you establish purity in your system at night, you will get a little conscious sleep, although not the kind that you will have when you have meditated for six or eight hours a day. Without some purity, what most of us call sleep is not sleep at all. It is death. During sleep we live in the world of the dead, the world of inertia and inconscience.

Question: Is it true that the soul flies to different planes during sleep?

Sri Chinmoy: There are three states of consciousness. *Susupti*, which you can call the dreamless state, is the purest, deepest, highest sleep. Then there is *Swapan*, the dream state, and finally *Jagriti*, wakefulness. In deep sleep, the soul gets the opportunity to fly from one plane of consciousness to another. We have many layers of consciousness inside our being, but when we are working, talking and mixing with others in the hustle and bustle of the world, the inner being is crushed and the soul does not get the opportunity to fly. We are in the outer world, and all kinds of silly things come into our outer mind; all is restlessness. But in deep sleep, the entire being is silenced and the soul can fly like a bird from one plane of consciousness to another. When the soul makes this flight without any obstruction, all the doors and windows in our inner being are automatically opened up. When the inner doors are all open and the soul is flying, at that time the outer being becomes one with the Divine and experiences the consciousness of Delight.

Now, how can an aspirant consciously have that feeling of oneness during sleep? It is through constant meditation. There is no other way. Otherwise when you become one with your Highest in your sound sleep, you will not be aware of it. You may be aware for a few seconds, or when you come back from that state of consciousness in the morning, but this does not necessarily happen. You are usually not aware of being totally united with the Highest when you are having the experience, so how can you expect to feel it hours later? The only way to be aware of that feeling, or to have the experience of oneness, is through constant aspiration, constant meditation.

From the golden morn
To the fiery noon
I pray to God.

From the fiery noon
To the retiring eve
I meditate on God.

From the retiring eve
To the starry night
I contemplate on God.

From the starry night
To the Golden Dawn
I sleep with God.

6

A Fountain
of Limitless Energy

A life that has no life-energy
Daily meets serious tragedies.
A life that has life-energy
Is the complete song
Of God's Satisfaction-Ecstasy.

Question: How can I have more energy?

Sri Chinmoy: You can have more energy by challenging something or someone. That does not mean you will fight against another human being. You are not fighting with anything outside. The one whom you are going to challenge is inside you – inside your body, inside your vital, inside your mind. If anything in your own life is dissatisfying you, that is the thing you have to challenge. Challenge your mind or your vital if they are not satisfying you. As soon as you challenge them, you will muster all your courage and energy. Otherwise your energy remains dormant.

Anything in your life that dissatisfies you, you have to challenge and fight like a hero. A hero will stand in front of you and say, "Either you listen to me and change your way of life or I will destroy you!" Then you will say, "No, I do not want to be destroyed! I want to be illumined." Anything that has to be illumined, you will challenge and illumine. Anything that has to be discarded, you will discard. And anything that has to be accepted into your life, you will accept. In order to get a large supply of energy, any dissatisfaction has to be challenged. Dissatisfaction takes away all our joy and energy.

Question: Can you tell me the relationship between soul and energy?

Sri Chinmoy: Energy is something fluid: like consciousness, it spreads itself everywhere in an infinite expanse. Energy is like the immense expanse of water in the ocean. It is a dynamic liquid in constant flux. If you enter into the inner world, you will see that energy is flowing and very dynamic. The soul, on the other hand, can take any form it likes. One moment it can be smaller than an atom and the next moment it can be vaster than the Vast.

Energy and the soul must go together. If there is no divine energy in the soul, then the soul cannot manifest anything. Again, if there is energy in the being but the consciousness of the soul is not brought forward, then realisation will not take place. So the two are interlinked. For realisation, energy needs the soul; and for manifestation, the soul needs energy.

Question: How is consciousness related to cosmic energy?

Sri Chinmoy: Cosmic energy is flowing consciously and constantly through consciousness, but at times the earthbound consciousness does not allow the cosmic energy to flow through it. At that time the seeker in the human being cannot make any progress.

Question: Do the body, mind and heart function differently when they function with the light of the soul?

Sri Chinmoy: Certainly, they do act differently; that is to say, they act divinely when they function with the light of the soul. With different eyes they see the truth, with different hearts they feel the truth. Always they function differently in the sense that they are tinged with God's Light. Their act of seeing and feeling is done through the play of energy. This energy is totally different from the usual physical energy. That is why we call it spiritual energy or cosmic energy. Cosmic energy is totally different from physical energy. When we draw in cosmic energy even for four or five minutes, we can overcome the need for rest or sleep most effectively. It is also the cosmic energy that quenches our inner thirst for Truth and Light most adequately.

Question: Could you speak about ways to cultivate intensity when you want to conquer obstacles to reach a goal?

Sri Chinmoy: There are two ways we can use. The first approach is through prayer. We have to pray to the Supreme, "Please, please bless me with intensity. Please give me abundant intensity." This is the first way. For a few days or a few months you can try this way.

The second way is to enter into your highest meditation. When you reach your absolutely highest meditation, just for two or three seconds utter the word 'intensity' with utmost will-power. When you utter the word 'intensity', like a bullet, intensity will enter into you. Not only will it enter into you, but it will also go out of you. Then this intensity will act like a miracle in your life. But ordinary meditation will not do. It has to be your own highest meditation.

You give more value to perfection than you do to intensity. Since you are aiming at perfection, crying for perfection at every moment, do not separate perfection from intensity. Try to have two wings in your spiritual life. If you care only for perfection, perfection, perfection, then there will be only one wing. You are aiming at perfection, but that perfection may be only according to your way of thinking. Somebody else may say that what you call perfection is nothing but imperfection. When you are aiming at perfection in your outer or inner life, since that is what you prefer, try to unite that goal with the eagerness you have for intensity. You already care for perfection. Now you should also care for intensity to the same extent. Where there is intensity, then the sense of perfection will automatically be there.

Question: What is the relationship between eagerness and intensity?

Sri Chinmoy: You have to value time. You have to feel that you have a higher goal, and that goal is still far away. Always intensity will increase if you feel that you have to go far, very far. Otherwise you will not budge an inch. Let us say that you are now in kindergarten and you have to get a Master's degree or Ph.D. If you are not ready, willing or eager to study, you may take quite a few years just to complete kindergarten. Later on you may become a school drop-out. This is what happens when eagerness is missing. Once you start your journey, your aim should be to reach the goal as soon as possible.

Eagerness has the power to create intensity. You can say eagerness is the penultimate step and intensity is the ultimate step. If you have eagerness to do something, you can invoke intensity inside that eagerness. Otherwise, right from the beginning you will be so relaxed and feel that you have Eternity at your disposal. Every day we have to feel that we have been given the chance to accomplish everything. If we cannot accomplish everything today, then tomorrow will come with the same opportunity. But if we feel that since it is something very difficult, we can take ten years or twenty years to accomplish it, that ten years will pass and we may not accomplish anything. Every day we have to have the adamantine will-power to achieve everything we want to achieve.

Incapacity comes from idleness.
Idleness is the acceptance
Of death's invitation.

Question: What is the relationship between eagerness and perseverance?

Sri Chinmoy: Eagerness expedites everything; it goes faster than the fastest. With eagerness we can climb up the Himalayas. But sometimes eagerness gives up when it meets obstacles and hurdles in life. With all eagerness we try something once, twice, three times, and then we give up. We approach somebody to ask for this or that, but after two or three attempts we feel it is beneath our dignity to approach that person again. Then we fail. But if perseverance comes to join eagerness, then we are saved.

When somebody succeeds, others may say, "Oh, he was lucky." But it is not luck. Previously, this person may have failed over and over again; many times he may have been unlucky to the extreme. But unlike others, he did not give up, and then finally he succeeded.

Many people are eager, but after two days their eagerness disappears. Two days is more than enough for them. If they do not succeed in two days, they will bring me the report: "I tried so hard, but it cannot be done." To succeed, we have to maintain our eagerness day after day. Eagerness can move mountains. But if eagerness cannot do something, then perseverance and patience are needed.

Our body does not listen to us because we do not listen to our soul. If we will listen to our soul, the body also will listen to us.

Enthusiasm is energy.
Energy defeats
Failure-life.

Enthusiasm has success
In it.
Enthusiasm is progress
In itself.

Enthusiasm has the capacity
To catch fire
In the very depths
Of my inner being.

Despondency can be fatal!
Enthusiasm is a divine spark
Within us
To challenge the pride of ignorance
Around us.

Dynamism and enthusiasm

May my life be found
Between dynamism-volcano
And enthusiasm-flood.

Question: How can we be more dynamic?

Sri Chinmoy: The dynamism that you want comes directly from the soul's light. Real dynamism is not aggression; real dynamism is the soul's light and our adamantine will. It is not that dynamism is found in the soul's light or in our adamantine will. No! The soul's light and our adamantine will are one and inseparable with divine dynamism. But we notice them at three different places. Dynamism we see in the vital world – not in the impure or emotional vital, but in the higher vital world. Here everything is like one big wave after another. They are not waves of destruction, but waves of boundless Light, Peace and Bliss.

As dynamism is the life-breath of the higher vital world, light, the soul's light, is the life-breath of the psychic world, the heart's world. The aspiring heart always wants to identify itself with something vast, and the soul's light is the breath of vastness.

Will also is found in a special place. Its location is in the third eye. And will is the life-breath of vision, the ultimate or universal vision of the future. In order to have constant dynamism, you have to be constantly aware of your goal and you have to feel that your goal is very close. It is not millions of miles away; it is around you, before you, in front of your nose. You have only to seek it consciously, grasp it and claim it. You have to always have the feeling that your goal is just before you, but that you are still unlucky and not able to see it. If you all the time feel that your goal is within easy reach, but that you don't know where it is, you will desperately cry for it and search for it, and naturally you will make an attempt to reach the goal. Then, while you are making the attempt, automatically your inner being is flooded with dynamism. If you feel that your goal is far, you become relaxed and feel that eternity is at your disposal. Then your inner dynamism doesn't come to the fore. But if you feel that what you want to grow into is just around you, only you have to use your conscious awareness to grasp it and claim it, then you will get dynamism. At that time, you will be constantly breathing in, consciously or unconsciously, the breath or soul of your goal, and dynamism will be yours.

Dynamism means the death of your lethargic life, the death of your ignorance life. The moment dynamism comes to the fore, immediately you see the death of lethargy, ignorance and anything else that prevents you from reaching your goal, growing into your goal and becoming your goal.

Exercise

Dynamism: Fire blazing all around

To increase your dynamism, meditate on flames. You can look at a candle flame or any other type of flame. Flames embody dynamism. If you look at a flame or imagine a flame, your lethargy will go away. Fire will burn all our lethargy or lack of enthusiasm. Anything that is undivine in us, fire will burn. If fire burns our lethargy, then automatically dynamism will come to the fore.

Fire has dynamism. That is why it keeps everything under control. Everything surrenders to fire. So always imagine flames or fire. If you imagine fire, you may think more of destruction than dynamism, but if you think of flames, climbing flames, then destruction will not come into your

mind. Flames take us upward. How can we go upward without becoming dynamic? If I want to climb a tree, if I want to climb a mountain, then I have to be dynamic. Flames show us the way. They are going up, up, up and touching the sky. So, to increase your dynamism, look at flames. That is the easiest and most effective way.

Question: How can one become more dynamic? The more there is to do, the slower I go. How can I overcome this?

Sri Chinmoy: If you find it difficult to bring down dynamic energy from above through meditation, no harm. You can become dynamic by repeating the word 'dynamism'. As soon as you utter the word 'dynamism', you are bound to feel tremendous strength either in your arms, or in your other limbs, or in your head or in your heart. Each time you repeat the word 'dynamism', a portion of your body will be surcharged with dynamism. Immediately you will feel a flow of dynamic energy in your legs, head, forehead, shoulders, or arms.

The word 'dynamism' has tremendous power, like the word 'peace'. If you can soulfully say 'peace', then automatically a part of your outer being will respond. And there will come a time when the inner being will also respond. Right now only a portion of you responds to the word 'dynamism'. But there will come a time when, from the sole of your foot to the top of your head, dynamism will flow when you repeat the word.

Question: How can we best deal with the anger that comes with dynamism?

Sri Chinmoy: Anger can easily be separated from dynamism, but only if you are in a good consciousness. If you are in a bad consciousness, an animal consciousness, then anger may appear not only in dynamism but even in the slowest movement.

When you are running at your top speed, is it not dynamism? At that time are you angry? No, you are running at top speed to win the race. So much dynamism is involved. Only if you are a very bad person will

you curse someone else who is going ahead of you. Otherwise, you will have no time to think of others.

So many things you do fast, very fast, with tremendous dynamism. At that time there is no anger involved. Only if pride enters while you are running very fast does anger come into the picture. Pride can take the form of anger. Again, this pride can easily be humiliated. If somebody is going ahead of you, your pride may be smashed.

> *When you work with enthusiasm,*
> *You are bound to establish*
> *A free access*
> *To an unending flow of life-energy*
> *And creative power.*

Question: Where is determination to be found? In which part of our being do we have to work on determination? Is it in the mind or the heart?

Sri Chinmoy: Determination can be found inside the mind. With determination, you can try to do many things. You can have the determination that says: "I will do something good. I will do something great. All bad things I will give up." But at any moment the determination that comes from the mind can be challenged by doubt, especially self-doubt. Then our determination is destroyed.

If you want to become a good person, a great person, or if you want to do something great, there is another way. That is the way of oneness. If you can identify yourself with something very strong, very powerful and very vast, then inside your oneness you will find all the positive qualities. When you use determination or will-power, you are entering into someone or something. Like a dagger, you are piercing into something. But the way of oneness is to just throw yourself into the vastness.

I always say that when a drop enters into the ocean, it becomes infinite, boundless – that drop you will no longer see.

Problems can be solved permanently only by identifying yourself with something very strong, very powerful, very vast. Look at the sky. How much vastness it has! Look at the ocean. How much power it has! Just throw yourself into the vastness or into the power. This is the wisest way and this way is also permanent.

Question: How can we work dynamically and soulfully, without rushing?

Sri Chinmoy: Think of your heart as an aeroplane and do not think of yourself as a car. An aeroplane goes much faster, but it is not rushing, whereas a car goes much slower and it is always rushing. So always think of the heart that is flying infinitely faster than the mind. When the mind runs, it is rushing. When the heart flies, it is just singing.

Question: How can we work quickly without tension?

Sri Chinmoy: Tension is in the mind, nowhere else. Inside the heart there is no tension. Even inside the knees or legs there is no tension; there is only pain. Real tension is inside the mind.

Tension goes away to a great extent if you can breathe in and out very slowly. If you can imagine that you are taking one full minute to breathe in and another full minute to breathe out, even though in reality it may not be true that you are taking that long, then your tension is bound to be released.

Question: How can we use the senses properly?

Sri Chinmoy: The proper fulfilment of the senses will come only from God. The body has the senses, but the body is not the owner; the real owner is God. If we can consciously go to the owner, then the owner will tell us how to utilise His possessions properly.

The senses are instruments, God's instruments. God originally entrusted us with these instruments, but we consciously chose not to ask God how to utilise these senses. Instead of asking God how to use the senses that He had given us, we asked the wrong teacher, ignorance. Or rather, before we actually asked ignorance to teach us, he came running to us to offer his wisdom. Since we gladly listened to him, we are now paying the penalty.

We could use our eyes, for example, to see the divine beauty in humanity and in all of God's creation. We could see the divine Light everywhere. But instead, what do we do with our eyes? We use our eyes either to possess the world or to reject it. When we see something that pleases us, immediately we try to possess it. And when we see something that displeases us, we try to reject it. The universe is all Light, but we do not see it. If we had taken the lesson from God on how to use the eyes, nose, ears and other sense organs, He would have given us proper instruction.

There is always time to receive instruction from God: better late than never. Each aspirant can consciously and devotedly pray to God to instruct him from within on how to use the senses. God will be most happy and proud to teach us. But we do not have to ask God about each sense individually. We need only approach God with sincere aspiration, and inside our aspiration He will see what we are crying for.

Life-energy and spiritual energy

Question: I do not understand what the word 'God' means. Can God be equivalent to energy?

Sri Chinmoy: God is not only equivalent to energy, God Himself is energy. But we have to know what aspect of God appeals to us. If God in the form of energy appeals to us, then God will come to us in the form of infinite energy. But if God in the form of a human being appeals to our mind and heart, He will come and stand right in front of us as a human being in a most luminous form.

The Buddha did not use the word 'God'; he used the word 'Nirvana'. Nirvana is Bliss, transcendental Bliss, and this Bliss is none other than God Himself. Again, we have to know what we actually want, what we care for. If we care for peace, then peace brings us satisfaction. This satisfaction brings still more peace that we can use in our daily life to satisfy ourselves and to bring forward our divine perfection. This divine perfection we can call God, or Peace, or any other divine quality.

Question: Can we draw upon the cosmic energy by going deep within ourselves?

Sri Chinmoy: Yes, we can draw upon the cosmic energy by entering into our deeper consciousness, the all-pervading consciousness, which is here, there, everywhere. There are various types of 'consciousness' in the spiritual worlds. It is the inner consciousness, the inmost consciousness, that touches the springs of the cosmic energy. If we can have a free access to our inmost consciousness, the cosmic energy is bound to come to the fore if you go deep within, it comes like a spring, a never-failing spring. And when it comes, it permeates the whole body.

Unfortunately we look at the spiritual life with our outer eyes. It is here that we make our mistake. But if we look at the inner life with our heart's feeling and our soul's light, then we see that the inner life has already housed the outer life, energised the outer life and perfected the outer life. The deeper we go within, the greater will be our fulfilling and fruitful achievement without.

Question: How can we effectively channel physical energy into spiritual energy?

Sri Chinmoy: We have to know that this physical energy has a source. It has only one source, and that source is the spiritual energy. As long as we remain in the body-consciousness, we are not aware of this, but when we go deep within, we see that spiritual energy is the source of the physical, vital and mental energy. When the spiritual energy left its Source and entered into the physical, it was somewhat polluted. It was unable to maintain its pristine purity.

What we need is purity on the inner plane and dedication on the outer plane. If we aspire, we will be able to purify the physical energy. Outer dedication comes through gradual inner purification and inner awareness. When we have both inner purity and outer dedication, then the spiritual energy enters into the physical energy, and the physical energy at that time becomes an added strength to the spiritual energy.

> *Life is not rest*
> *But a dynamic flow*
> *Of cosmic energy.*

Question: Could you say something about self-control in the body?

Sri Chinmoy: In the spiritual life self-control is most important, significant and fruitful. No self-control, no self-realisation! Self-control is the most difficult concept to practise. If one wants to have self-control, one has to surrender oneself to the Source. This Source is Light; this Source is God.

A child wants to have many things – many useless, harmful things. But the mother knows that if she gives the child these things, he will be ruined. And just because mother and child are one, the mother will also be ruined. So the mother does not fulfil the child's countless unlit, destructive desires. Similarly, the body is a child. If you fulfil all its desires and demands, in the long run your life will be ruined.

Why does the body not listen to us when we try to control it? The answer is very simple. Our body does not listen to us because we do not listen to our soul. If we will listen to our soul, the body also will listen to us.

Question: It seems to me that it takes a certain amount of energy and desire to follow the path of your teachings. And what about the rank beginner on it? Sometimes you can't muster enough energy to get yourself going!

Sri Chinmoy: You are right. Not only to follow my path, but to follow any spiritual path, one has to have some energy, some spiritual energy and aspiration. But I think that if one has to wait for this dynamic and spiritual energy, then one will never start one's journey. So if you really want the spiritual life, I say: throw yourself into the inner life. Don't look either backwards or sideways. Look ahead and jump into the sea of spirituality. Start from where you are. If you have limited energy, if your aspiration is insignificant, then I wish to say something to you. Go deep within. You will get to the inner well, the source of aspiration.

You cannot become a multimillionaire overnight. You have to start with a penny. Similarly if you have a little aspiration, if you really care for God, then start uttering God's name once a day, early in the morning. Gradually you can transform the whole day, into a repetition of God's name and make real headway towards your self-discovery. If you have a sincere cry for God, then you can start your spiritual journey, no matter where you are or what you have.

> Enthusiasm is energy.
> Energy defeats
> Failure-life.

Exercise

Overcoming lethargy

The quickest way is by repeating 'Supreme' as fast as possible. You do not have to shout at the top of your lungs, but you have to be able to hear it; do not do it in silence. You can be seated in your room or walking in a silent place where nobody is going to hear you, but you should not do it while lying down.

While you are chanting 'Supreme', starting with your toes imagine everything that is inside you. Think of your muscles, nerves, blood or anything that you want, and try to feel that the Supreme is entering into that particular part of your body. Then move to other parts of your body. You do not have to see what is inside your legs or your heart or your brain. Only imagine that something is there, and that that very thing is being touched by the word 'Supreme'. If lethargy has already stationed itself inside your knee or shoulder or somewhere else, that portion of the being has to be touched by the very Presence of the Supreme. So each time you say "Supreme", chanting as fast as possible, try to feel that the Power of the Supreme, the Life of the Supreme and the Divinity of the Supreme are entering into you.

This is one of the most effective ways to conquer lethargy while walking or doing something. When you want to conquer lethargy, that is not the time for you to enter into deep meditation; only let the dynamic flow of your chanting percolate through your entire body. If you enter into a higher type of meditation or prayer and are trying to be dynamic, you may succeed; but when the prayer or meditation is over, the dynamism will disappear. But the Supreme's Name you can repeat any time.

Question: How can we overcome our unwillingness?

Sri Chinmoy: If we know that we are supposed to do something good, then we have to take unwillingness as a naughty boy, as a naughty little brother. You are telling your little brother, who is four years old, "Come and eat! It is time for you to eat." But he is fooling around and he does not want to eat. So what do you do? You grab this little brother and say, "You *must* eat. Otherwise I will not allow you to remain here." First he will start misbehaving. He will strike you, kick you and do all kinds of things. But when he sees that you are much stronger than he is, then he will surrender. So, unwillingness we can take as an individual, as a very, very naughty and mischievous boy.

You have to feel that your inner strength is infinitely greater than the strength of this little mischievous boy. You know that your strength – your physical strength, vital strength and mental strength, your strength in everything – far surpasses the strength of that little fellow. So you grab him. First he will be naughty; he will strike you. Then he will become tired. He will see that you are stronger, infinitely stronger, and then he will see that what you are saying is the right thing. When he is ignorant, he does not want to do the right thing, but afterwards he will do it gladly.

You have to be very, very strict with unwillingness. Early in the morning, if you are supposed to get up at six o'clock but unwillingness comes or lethargy comes, then immediately just jump up on the bed and start raising your arms and legs. You have to be abrupt with unwillingness, quicker than the quickest! Unwillingness is something that has developed very slowly inside us, and it is very, very destructive. The source of unwillingness is the mind, not the body or the vital. It comes from the mind that has become very idle and lethargic. So, early in the morning or any time, bring the heart forward and make yourself feel that the strength of your heart is much more powerful than the strength of your unwilling mind.

Unwillingness will fight, as I said. The little brother will fight, but when he sees that you are much stronger, then he will surrender and feel that what you are saying is the right thing for him to do. So, always take unwillingness as a mischievous, naughty boy.

Question: How can we create more energy inside ourselves so we can aspire more?

Sri Chinmoy: While you are breathing you have to imagine and feel that an abundance of life-energy is entering into you. Life-energy is nothing but aspiration. You know how much air you are allowing your body to accept while you are inhaling. If you feel that a certain amount of breath you are inhaling in the normal way, then while you are meditating you have to feel that each breath that you are breathing in is at least ten times larger than usual. This breath creates an abundant supply of energy. When you are consciously trying to bring in more energy, you have to feel that a surplus, an abundant supply of energy is entering. This energy is nothing but aspiration, an immediate increase of aspiration.

Question: Sometimes after I have a very high meditation at the Centre or in a meditation hall, I have so much energy that I really want to run around. I do not want to stay in the hall.

Sri Chinmoy: Your whole being has been energised in such a powerful manner that afterwards you are bursting with spiritual energy. When this energy outburst comes, it is usually at one particular place, such as the chest area above the heart – not actually in the heart itself. Or it may happen that at one particular part of your head, such as your forehead, you will feel energy is trying to come out of your head, as if something is about to burst.

If you are alone, at that time you can chant, you can read my poems aloud, or you can sing. If you are with others, then in silence very soulfully sing some spiritual songs that you know. Let this energy, which comes in a very exuberant way, flow from the soles of your feet to the crown of your head like a river. Do not try to hold it. Let it not be accumulated at one particular place. Let it take the form of liquid energy. You will see that automatically you will become calm and quiet again. By consciously trying to help the energy flow from one place to another inside you, you will be able to enjoy that divine energy.

> Just silence the mind.
> Lo!
> Cosmic energy enters
> Into our entire being,
> And tremendous energy
> Flows in and through us.

Exercise

Life-energy entering the crown chakra

While chanting 'Aum', please feel that life–energy, divine energy, is entering into you through your crown centre. The breath that you breathe in through the nose is very limited; but if you can imagine that there is a big hole in the top of your head and that life-energy, cosmic energy, is entering into your body through that big hole, then naturally you will be able to accelerate your purification and increase your aspiration and hunger for God, truth, light and bliss.

Question: What is the highest kind of purity I can aspire to?

Sri Chinmoy: The highest kind of purity is purity in the physical, that is to say, the lower physical, the emotional vital. The region below the navel has to be purified totally. Human beings have purity to some extent in the heart; in the mind there is very little. In the vital, purity is mixed up with impurity; there dynamism and aggression work together. So whenever you feel aggression, it is impurity, and when you feel divine dynamism, it is purity. Below the vital is the physical. There, due to inertia and sloth, darkness reigns supreme. Where there is darkness, impurity is bound to play its role.

You have to aspire for purity in the gross physical. How can you do it? It is through constant prayer and your constant inner cry for Light. Light and darkness cannot stay together. Impossible! Just as fear and courage cannot go together, similarly purity and impurity cannot stay together.

> *Carry on the struggle.*
> *You will eventually win.*
> *Strive with vigour.*
> *You will quite certainly win.*
> *Depend entirely on God's Grace.*
> *You will immediately win.*

7

New Adventures
in Old Age

Enthusiasm-fountain
Is nothing other than
A God-seeker's ignorance-daring
And ignorance-conquering youth-fire.

Old age is no obstacle. Churchill embarked on painting at a very old age. There are many, many world-famous people who became great in their old age. Even Tagore started painting just a few years before he passed away. Previously, he was all the time writing books. Only at the end of his life, he became an artist. At what point people can bloom, we do not know. That is why we say "late bloomers"!

Then again, when we become old, we will get new joy, new inspiration and new delight if we can continue with the good things that we have been doing for years. We may do the same thing every day, but there will be new joy awaiting us every day with our continued practice.

For example, when Pablo Casals was 95 years old, he was still practising his cello every day. He felt just the same as always. Once someone asked him, "Why do you practise at your age? You have become the greatest cellist. Now you can rest!" Casals answered, "You want me to rest? You do not want me to make any progress? Every day I am playing the cello and I have been playing for years and years, ever since my childhood. Every day I feel I have made some progress."

When inspiration comes, we must pay no attention to age – whether we are eight or eighty. We also have to continue as long as we live on

earth with the good things that we have been doing. Since
Pablo Casals played the cello regularly, every day for him was like
a new dawn, a new sunrise.

New creative life can start at any age. There is no age limit. But if you
want to continue, if you want to make progress and get ever more joy
from your creativity, then you have to practise regularly and punctually.

His youth remains,
Although
He is ninety years old.

His youth remains,
Because
He loves the quintessence of life:
Oneness-light.

His youth remains,
Because
God has always much work
To accomplish in him,
Through him, on earth.

The younger you can become, the faster will be your progress. This is
absolutely no joke! I am fast approaching sixty-five years of age.
I shall do a few more things in this lifetime, which I could not do in my
adolescent years. I have already done the head balance, which I could
never do, even when I was a champion athlete. And there are five or
six more things I shall do in this incarnation, which, at the time of my
athletic career, I could not do.

188

If you sincerely want to make faster progress, you have to have a childlike heart. By any means, I am begging each and every disciple to bring back your childhood consciousness. Your childhood consciousness is not silly, no. When you were a little boy or a little girl, you were a most beautiful flower. Then over the years age descends on us. We become fruits and then the fruits become rotten. So let us not grow into fruits. Let us only feel that every day we are blossoming, blossoming. Every day we shall blossom and place ourselves at the Feet of our Lord Beloved Supreme.

To each and everyone I am saying, try to make yourself young. Feel that you are only seven years old if you want to make the fastest progress. I assure you, this is the most effective way to make the fastest progress. Do not think that you have to be childish. It is not childish but childlike that we wish to become. God Himself is childlike. When we are childish, we do many, many stupid things. But to go back to our childhood days is not a stupid thing. If you really want to make progress in your life, this is the only way to think of yourself – as young as possible.

It is the mind that makes us feel we are too old, we are useless. This mind has to be silenced by the will of the heart, by the will of the soul. God is always asking us to silence the mind, the mind that tells us we are too old, we are helpless, we are useless, we can do nothing. We must tell the mind that says we can do nothing that the mind itself is nothing and we are everything.

It is the light of the soul that can illumine the mind. True, it is a very, very long process, but the mind can be illumined eventually. If you silence the mind, the mind becomes like a tame and faithful dog. Now the mind is all the time barking and biting and frightening us: we cannot do this, we cannot do that.

Age is in the mind; age is not in the body. When we think that we are old, that is the end, the very end, of our journey. Every day at every moment only think that you are a seven-year-old or a nine-year-old or ten-year-old, but do not think that you are over thirty. Do not make it into thirty-one and absolutely not into forty-one! If you cannot make yourself into a seven–year–old child, then at the maximum think of thirteen. Just imagine! Imagination is a reality of its own. Imagination is a world of its own, but you have to bring down that world every day or you have to enter into that world.

I always say that physical fitness is of paramount importance. Inside the body is the soul. The soul is not somewhere else. Inside the body-temple is the shrine. If we do not keep the temple in proper condition, the shrine will be totally ruined. So take exercise, lose weight, those who have to lose weight. Those who are physically weak, become strong. Keep your body fit if you really want to make progress.

There are some schools of thought that say the body is useless. Ramana Maharshi and others said to meditate and meditate. I also say the same, but since you are following my path, I must add that the body also plays a most significant role in our spiritual life. Let us strive for physical fitness, not world championships! We shall progress, we shall transcend and transcend, but our goal is physical fitness.

There are some men and women, especially some women, who have surrendered to age. I am telling you that you have to surrender to the heart, not to the mind. If you surrender to your heart, you can make progress every day. If you surrender to your mind, your progress will come to a complete halt.

Even if you do not want to take exercise early in the morning, try to make yourself feel that you are quite young. Just go outside and see what happens. Then, while you are walking, try to walk a little faster. While you are doing anything, make the movement faster. Bring back your childlike days when you used to run and play with utmost joy.

God's message to the older generation:
"As long as you remain on earth,
You must realise that your days
Are equally as important
As those of the younger generation
Whose hearts are all hope
And whose lives are all promise."

Question: What is more important for older people: cheerfulness or wisdom-light?

Sri Chinmoy: Cheerfulness and wisdom-light are inseparable. If you have wisdom-light, then naturally you will be cheerful. You have to be cheerful in order to be always ready to receive God's Light. If you are eager to receive God's Love, Light and everything that God wants to give you, you will get them sooner than otherwise. Again, if you are cheerful, that is the height of your spiritual wisdom. So wisdom gives us cheerfulness, and cheerfulness itself is wisdom.

Cheerfulness
Indicates
The nearness of God.

Question: Do you have any special message for people over 40?

Sri Chinmoy: O children of the Supreme, you are not the children of the past but the children of the Eternal Now. You are the children of the ever-glowing Heart of the Supreme, the ever-flowing Soul of the Supreme and the ever-illumining Body of the Supreme.

Like God,
You must not waste any time.
Like God's,
Your aspiration-life must not have
Any retirement plan.

Question: What is the difference, from a spiritual point of view, between an old person and a child?

Sri Chinmoy: It is a child, not an old person, who makes progress in life. Old people do not care for progress. But mere years do not make a person old. Somebody who is sixty or seventy years of age may have the enthusiasm, inner joy and inspiration of a child. Again, there will be people seventeen, eighteen or nineteen years old who have no aspiration, no inspiration, no dynamism. If a boy of nineteen does not have the capacity to draw something from the world or to offer something to the world, if he does not care for the world and feels that he does not need anything from the world, then he is ninety-nine years old in spirit. On the other hand, if somebody of ninety-nine wants to learn the inner language – the language of divine love, the language of divine peace, the language of divine wisdom, the language of divine light – then he is a child in spirit. In the spiritual life we are not concerned with earthly years but with an individual's inner eagerness to do something and to become something – to become a child of God.

If you really want to become a child, then you have to feel that there is always something to learn and that God is there to teach you. In the spiritual life you are learning something every day, every hour, every minute, every second from our divine Father. If you constantly have the feeling that you are learning in the inner world, there is no end to the God-divinity that you can receive and achieve.

If you do not throw cold water
On your aspiration-heart,
You will never become old.

Question: It seems that adults are always worried about things, but not children.

Sri Chinmoy: Because a child lives in the heart, he always feels that his mother or his father will take care of him. All the time he feels that there is protection, there is guidance, there is assistance. So naturally he has confidence in his life. Because he is always in the heart, he feels that there is no need, which his parents will not fulfil. If he lived in the mind, he would immediately think, "Oh, perhaps my father will not be able to do this. Perhaps my mother will not be there to help me." Then he would become fearful, doubtful and anxious. But a child does not live in the mind. Similarly, if you want to have a childlike spirit, no matter how old you are, you have to feel that there is Someone with infinitely more Wisdom-Light who is constantly thinking of you, guiding you and protecting you, and that this Person is God.

He who cares more for the intellect than for the heart, he who cares more for the outer achievement than for the inner achievement, he who cares more for society around him than for God within him, can never act like a child. A true child lives all the time in the heart, whereas a grown-up is all the time in the mind. In the mind there is no love. Real love can be found only inside the flower-heart. The flower-heart tries all the time to make others happy. Because God has the flower-heart of a child, He is trying all the time to make us happy. A child's flower-heart is a divine heart. If we remain in the outer world, we see children as ordinary human beings. But if we go within, then we immediately see that children embody all the divine qualities of God. At that time we see children as true miracles – as divine instruments, as flowers of God.

Be spontaneous like a child.
A child does not try
To acquire anything unnatural.
He does not try to be somebody
Or something else.
He approaches God in a natural way.

Question: As I am getting older, I am finding it harder and harder to accept my age. Can you say something that will allow me to better accept the fact?

Sri Chinmoy: The moment you think of your old age, you destroy all your inspiration, aspiration, joy and enthusiasm. The moment you think of your old age, that very moment is your death. You have to feel that everything is a series of experiences. Do not take life and death as two separate things: this is life, that is death – no! Death is just a passage we are going through. There is life, and on the way we meet death. In the Eternal Life, there is life, then death, then again life. It is a game that is going on.

Do not think of your old age. Think of your life as a road that is twenty-six miles long – a marathon – and then divide it into four or five stages. In the beginning, say for twenty years, you were learning and learning and learning. Then, in the second stage, you were learning and at the same time you were sharing your wisdom. Now you are in the third or fourth stage. So you have to see what you could do at the age of twenty, what you could do at the age of fifty and what you can do at the age of sixty. Do not think that what you did at the age of twenty is infinitely more important than what you are doing at the age of sixty. When you were twenty years old, God experienced Himself in and through you as a great student. Then He experienced Himself as a budding professor. When you turned forty, God experienced something totally different in and through you. At the age of sixty, He is experiencing something else again.

It is a game. At this moment, God is playing a particular role in and through you. In a few years, in the same Cosmic Play, He can play another role. After another twenty years, He can play yet another role. We make a serious mistake by feeling that when we are fifty or sixty the role that God is playing through us is sometimes not as important as the role that He gave us to play at the age of twenty. We have to feel that whatever role God plays through us at the age of twenty, forty or sixty is equally important. For Him, sixty is not old age. After the age of eighty or even one hundred, when you go away to the other world, you will see that there He is still playing His role inside your soul.

We always see the physical. We talk about our physical age, but the truth is that the moment we take a physical body, death becomes inevitability. We may die tomorrow or the day after tomorrow. Again, inside the body, if you can be in touch with the soul, then you can take the body as a toy. You are playing with the toy, and then afterwards you are finished with the toy. This is always how it should be.

If you take it in that way, then the mind does not come into the picture. Use only your heart. Otherwise your mind will come forward and expect you to be able to do what you did at the age of twenty, to have the same youth and enthusiasm. But now that you are more advanced in years, wisdom is dawning in your life. When you are at the age of sixty, then you have the wisdom to say, "Over the years, I have not prayed enough to God. I came from Him; I will go back to Him. At that time, will I be able to show Him my physical capacity, my mental capacity or my vital capacity? God will say, 'Enough! I have seen your physical capacity, your vital capacity and your mental capacity. Now show Me your psychic capacity, your heart's capacity, your inner capacity. Let Me see how much you have really loved Me.' "

You are at the age of sixty, but you have to forget about being sixty. You are playing a new role; you have got a new task. How much are you ready to pray and meditate and lead the spiritual life? Do not think of all the mistakes that you have made as mistakes as such, but think that you have played a certain role and now it is over. If you start thinking of all your past mistakes, then it will only be an added burden for you. Instead just say, "I went there, and I had an experience." Now wisdom has to come to the fore, and you will not do the same thing again because you did not find your goal inside those experiences. Now that you are sixty, only think of spreading your wings. You are already flying, but you have to spread your wings. How? By loving God and serving Him inside mankind. You should not say, "I am old. I do not have the capacity I used to have." Instead you should say, "God does not want me to have my former capacity because God does not want to play that role in me any more. Now He wants me to dive deep within, as deep as possible. He wants me to have inner experiences to share with mankind." Is that not infinitely more important than what you did in your youth?

Again, everything has its own importance. The experiences that God gave you at the age of twenty or forty are also valuable. If a child does not have enthusiasm at the age of four or five, then will he get it at the age of fifty or sixty? Even if he gets it, it will not be the same because it is not coming slowly from a tender age. All of a sudden the tree is looking nice but while the tree was growing, when it was a tender plant, it did not look nice at all. So, every phase of life is equally important because our good qualities must develop slowly, slowly, slowly. If the seed does not germinate and become a tender plant, how can it become a huge banyan tree? Similarly, how can we think of becoming one with God if we have not prayed and meditated for many years? Before we took human incarnation, we were one with God. But He made us a tiny drop. Then He told us to expand, expand, expand and become the ocean. It is a continuous growth, a continuous expansion.

The mind is never to be used at any time. If the mind is used, then you are finished. When you are ten years old, the mind will make you feel that you are as old as ninety years! Only think that at this particular stage of life you are supposed to do something. Then after ten or fifteen years you are supposed to do something else. Continuously a new game is starting, a new part you have to play. Each time you are given a new role, you have to play it well. When you become a huge tree, at that time more responsibility comes. A tree has to give so much, so much. Under the tree at first only one pilgrim can stay. Later many individuals can come and stay. Finally, the tree has to feel the responsibility of giving shade, protection and shelter to all. The higher you go, the more shelter, protection and illumination you have to give to others. In terms of human age, you may be only sixty or seventy, but in terms of divine light and divine wisdom you will become hundreds and hundreds of years old.

Age does not matter, unless you feel that both the giver in you and the taker in you have come to a complete halt.

When it is a matter of light, there are no earthly years involved. Light, delight, peace and so on do not belong to an earthly calendar. They came from Infinity, they remain in Infinity and they will always remain in Infinity. We have to consciously try to grow into that Infinity. Our life-river is flowing, flowing, flowing and entering into the ocean. Do not take the life-river as something that can be divided into years. It is a oneness-flow that is going towards the infinite Light. The important thing is not to use the mind when age is descending upon you. Only use the heart. Just say, "At this point I have to blossom in this way; at that time I had to blossom in a different way. A few years from now

I will have to blossom in a totally different way." Each moment has its own most significant beauty. When the time comes, when your life-flower is fully blossomed, then it will be able to give much more joy and fragrance to mankind and be of more help to sincerely aspiring seekers.

True, you have worked hard
For many years.
But you must aspire until the end.
There is no such thing as a pension
In the spiritual life.

Our Indian scriptures say health is our religion. Health is the code of life. Village people walk two miles to market, but city people are in trouble. I strongly feel that after the age of forty or fifty, you have to spend a minimum of three hours a day doing exercise and taking care of your health.

Definitely
God does not want
To hear from you
That you are too old!

Question: When playing sports, should you think of yourself as a child?

Sri Chinmoy: While playing sports, do not think of yourself as twenty-five or thirty years old. Feel that you are seven years old. At the age of six or seven, a child does not sit; he just runs here and there with such enthusiasm. So feel in your heart the enthusiasm of a young child and identify yourself with the Source of his enthusiasm.

I forget
That God is an old man
And that He can easily advise me
In everything I do and say.

I forget
That I am a little child
And that I can play with Him
Any time I want to.

Question: Does age deter strength training?

Sri Chinmoy: Unfortunately it does. But if a sincere seeker, on the strength of his sleepless love of God, can establish a free access to the constant newness, freshness and fulness of God's infinite Light and Delight, then the weaknesses and limitations of age can be surmounted, and the seeker will get the message-light to go beyond age.

A true God-lover
Does not grow older,
He only becomes wiser.

Question: Can you tell us something about your experience while you participated in the Senior Games[2]?

Sri Chinmoy: Here there is no competitive spirit. Here there is no greed. Here there is only joy. It is through joy that we are going to transcend ourselves.

At the age of thirteen or fourteen I ran. It is quite natural for a teenager to run. But at the age of sixty-five if I run, it means I am trying to maintain some joy, some enthusiasm. I am also trying to keep my body fit. When we are young, running is all competition; we want to defeat everybody and become the winner. Here the philosophy is totally different. If we can have cheerfulness and happiness, then that is our best achievement. At this age to do anything happily, cheerfully and self-givingly is most difficult.

Here I am competing with myself in order to maintain my inner joy and outer joy. When I run, I try my best to bring forward the enthusiasm that I had when I was a teenager. I try my best, but most of the time it does not come. The lethargy of the body does not allow me to bring forward the same quickness, alertness and promptness. I am imagining something, but the reality is somewhere else. When I was young, I did not have to imagine anything. I only used my capacity, which became reality. At that time, reality was pushing me forward. Now imagination is desperately trying to push me forward.

Our philosophy is the philosophy of self-transcendence. No matter how old we are, we are trying to increase our capacities and transcend our achievements.

Age does not matter, unless you yourself wish to sing your own swansong long before it is due.

Question: Do you feel nervous when you compete in senior games like this?

Sri Chinmoy: Nervousness comes only when we feel that we are the doers. If Somebody else is the Doer, then we are just the witnesses. It is up to Him whether we are successful or not. We have only to be good instruments. But if we feel that we are doing it ourselves, then we are in trouble. We will have no sleep, no sleep.

In my youth, when I used to excel in sports, when I was the decathlon champion of our spiritual community, I was nervous for a few years in the beginning. But then I saw that my brothers and sisters were infinitely more nervous than I was on our sports days. They took my nervousness from me.

Yesterday the Canadian boxer Donny Lalonde asked, "Sri Chinmoy, are you nervous?" I said, "I gave my nervousness many years ago to the athletics field." Now if I do not succeed or if I succeed, my success or my failure, because of my spiritual life, I place at the Feet of God. Only I have to be a good and pure instrument so that He can utilise me in His own Way. If I am not, then I will not be able to please Him in His own Way. So I will try to be a good person, at least for today. If I am not good, how will He act in and through me? The responsibility is His. My only responsibility is to keep my mind calm and quiet, vacant and pure. Again, some people find that extremely difficult. Because they do not have a calm mind, they are assailed by the forces of anxiety, worry and so on.

Here it is a family game in front of my brothers and sisters, my spiritual friends and my students. Do I have to worry? If I cannot succeed, they will sympathise with me. If I succeed, they will be so happy that their teacher has done it. I will not be the loser in any way because their sympathetic oneness with me is such that no matter what I do, they are one with me.

I am so lucky. Every time I get a very sympathetic audience. People come here for peace of mind. They do not come to see a weightlifter or bodybuilder. They know me only as a man of prayers for peace, love and harmony. They come to see me as their fellow compatriot in peace. They come here for a peaceful evening and not for anything else. Otherwise, they can go to Mr. Olympia and Mr. Universe competitions.

Here I am only competing with myself to show progress. If I can make progress at the age of sixty-eight, what is wrong with others? People at the age of fifty or sixty give up. I have students at the age of twenty-seven or twenty-eight who say they are too old! Then I have to scold them and do everything to inspire them. How can they be old at the age of twenty-seven? They feel that they cannot run as well as they used to. I say, "Then do something else. Keep running, but add something else as well. Why should you only be a runner?"

I was a runner. Now I have entered into weightlifting. Then sometimes I do painting or compose songs or write poems. Like that, God has given us so many opportunities. If we cannot do one thing, we can do something else.

Alas,
Many older seekers feel
That they have one foot in the grave,
Or that they can enjoy
Retirement-relaxation.
Absolutely untrue!
God wishes all His children,
Young and old,
To have the same sleepless determination,
Enthusiasm and willingness
To serve Him.

In the spiritual life there is no such thing as failure. We may fail, we may descend, we may have the so-called outer experience of failure. But this is not the real failure. The real failure is only when we give up and say: "This is an impossible task; no matter how many times I try, I fail." If I entertain this wrong feeling and give up, then I have accepted failure and become failure itself. I shall fail only when I give up – never, never before!

Hope does not surrender to
Old age.
Hope is always ready
To inspire and energise human beings
Irrespective of age.

8

Meditation and Breathing Techniques

Fundamentals of meditation

*M*editation is the eye that sees the Truth,
The heart that feels the Truth
And the soul that realises the Truth.

Meditation means conscious self-expansion. Meditation means one's conscious awareness of the transcendental Reality. Meditation means the recognition or the discovery of one's own true self. It is through meditation that we transcend limitation, bondage and imperfection.

Meditation is like going to the bottom of the sea, where everything is calm and tranquil. On the surface there may be a multitude of waves, but the sea is not affected below. In its deepest depths, the sea is all silence. When we start meditating, first we try to reach our own inner existence – that is to say, the bottom of the sea. Then, when the waves come from the outside world, we are not affected. Fear, doubt, worry and all the earthly turmoils will just wash away, because inside us is solid peace. Thoughts cannot touch us, because our mind is all peace, all silence, all oneness. Like fish in the sea, they jump and swim but leave no mark on the water. Like birds flying in the sky, they leave no trace behind them. So when we are in our highest meditation we feel that we are the sea, and the animals in the sea cannot affect us. We feel that we are the sky, and all the birds flying past cannot affect us. Our mind is the sky and our heart is the infinite sea. This is meditation.

Meditation is silence, energising and fulfilling. Silence is the eloquent expression of the inexpressible.

Question: What is the difference between going high and going deep in meditation?

Sri Chinmoy: There is a great difference in the methods of meditation, although ultimately height and depth become one. When we want to go deep in meditation, we start our journey from the spiritual heart. From there, deep is not downward or backward, but inward. We should feel that we are digging or travelling deep, deep, deep into our heart. It is not like digging downward far below our feet. No! Below the knees, the plane of inconscience starts. If we go downward, then it is not actually spiritual depth that we are getting but only the low, lower, lowest planes of consciousness. The spiritual heart is infinite, so there is no limit to how deep we can go. We can never go too deep; we can never touch the boundaries of the spiritual heart because it embodies the vast universe and, at the same time, it is larger and vaster than the universe.

When we want to go high in meditation, then our direction is upward. Our aspiration goes upward; we are climbing, climbing fearlessly toward the Highest. We must pass through the mind and through the thousand-petalled lotus at the top of the head. Again, the distance is infinite.

There is no end to our upward journey because we are travelling in Infinity. We are climbing toward the ever-transcending Beyond. In terms of distance, upward and inward are both infinite journeys toward one Goal, the Supreme.

We cannot go high by using only the mind, however. We must go beyond the mind and into the realm of the spiritual heart once more. The domain of the spiritual heart is infinitely higher and vaster than that of the very highest mind. Far beyond the mind is still the domain of the heart. The heart is boundless in every direction, so inside the heart is height as well as depth. The higher we can go, the deeper we can go. And again, the deeper we can go, the higher we can go. It works simultaneously.

Controlling the mind

If you meditate in the mind, you will be able to meditate for perhaps five minutes, and out of that five minutes, for one minute you may meditate very powerfully. After that you will feel your whole head getting tense. First you get joy and satisfaction, but then you may feel a barren desert. For five minutes you will get something, but if you want to go beyond that, you may feel nothing. If you meditate in the heart, a day will come when you start getting satisfaction. If you meditate in the heart, you are meditating where the soul is. True, the light, the consciousness of the soul permeates the whole body, but there is a specific place where the soul resides most of the time, and that is in the heart. If you want illumination, if your ultimate goal is illumination, you will get that illumination from the soul, which is inside the heart. When you know what you want and where to find it, the sensible thing is to go to that place. Otherwise, it will be like going to the hardware store to get groceries. If you concentrate on the mind you will be disappointed and disheartened. You will not get what you want because you have gone to the wrong place.

You have to be wise. There is a vast difference between what you can get from the mind and what you can get from the heart. The mind is limited; the heart is unlimited. Deep within us is infinite Peace, Light and Bliss. To get a limited quantity is an easy task. Meditation in the mind can give it to you. But you can get more if you meditate in the heart. Suppose you have the opportunity to work at two places. At one place you will earn two hundred dollars, and at the other place five hundred dollars. If you are wise, you will not waste your time at the first place.

Question: I have read about different methods of clearing my mind of outside thoughts, but it seems that the harder I try, the more difficult it becomes. As I understand it, if you are meditating properly, light or knowledge will come from outside sources if your mind is completely clear. Is this true?

Sri Chinmoy: Light and knowledge do not come from outside sources. They come from within. You have been focussing your attention on a particular object, and this is concentration. Meditation is something else. When you meditate you focus on Infinity, on something very vast, deep, sublime. You do not see an object; you try to grow into an infinite expansion. In concentration you focus on something small, but in meditation you throw yourself into something very vast.

You say that it is extremely difficult for you to meditate. That is because you are trying to meditate inside your mind. The very nature of the mind is to welcome ideas – good, bad, divine, undivine. But the nature of the heart is to try to become one with the ultimate Goal. To clear the mind is very hard, it is true. So the best thing you can do is try to bring the heart forward and illumine the mind with the light of the heart. It is always advisable to meditate in the heart. The love and oneness of the heart and soul will unite you with Divinity. When you are well established in the heart, on the strength of your aspiration, then you can enter into the physical mind to transform it. Otherwise, it is almost impossible to deal with the mind and go beyond the mind. Throw all the possessions of the mind into the heart. When you do this consciously, the heart is able to bring the light from the soul into the mind, or the soul will consciously offer light to the mind. Then the mind can be transformed and illumined. Always try to throw the mind into the heart. Then your meditation can be meaningful and fruitful every day. Otherwise, you can meditate for years and years and have no satisfaction, because the mind will never stop disturbing you. So please meditate on the heart and try to identify yourself spontaneously with something vast, something sublime, inside you. Once your identification is strong it will be extremely easy for you to meditate.

When you are trying to make your mind calm and quiet, you are concentrating. If you can concentrate on quieting your mind that is a wonderful thing. When you are successful in chasing away all the thoughts that disturb your mind, sooner or later your inner self will automatically come to the fore and stand right in front of you like the blazing sun clearing away the veil of clouds. Right now, the inner sun is overcast with clouds: thoughts, ideas, doubts, fears and so forth. When you can chase them away, you will see that the inner self is shining bright and radiant right in front of you. Please continue with what you are doing. It is a very good thing, and it will enable you to go farther, higher and deeper. Meditation will automatically be done by your inner being. Only try to concentrate regularly, faithfully and devotedly each day.

Take the mind as a monkey or an unruly child. The very nature of the monkey is to bite you. But you can either pay no attention to it, or if it continues to bother you, threaten and frighten it. But always reject it. As many times as it comes to you, chase it away or deliberately place your conscious awareness on something else. If you allow it to distract you, it will gain strength and continue to torture you.

During your meditation your mind may resist and obstruct you, but you have to feel that you have something superior to the mind, and that is your heart. Try to get help from your heart. If you feel that the help you are getting from the heart is not enough, then go to the highest, that is, to the soul. Feel that you have and are nothing but the soul. Sincerely repeat, "I am the soul, I am the soul." If you can repeat this soulfully for five minutes, the resistance of the physical mind will go away and only the heart and soul will exist for you.

If we want to control the mind with our will, it will be like asking a monkey not to bother us. The very nature of the monkey is to bite and pinch us. It is impossible to stop it. But we can bring to the fore the light of the soul, which has unlimited power. In the outer world, when somebody is superior in strength or power, he tries to punish the one that is bothering him. But in the spiritual life, the light of the soul and the light of the heart will not punish the mind. On the contrary, the light will act like a most affectionate mother. It will come forward and try to transform the mind. It will feel, as a mother does, that the imperfection of the child is its own imperfection. The heart will feel the obscurity, impurity and darkness of the mind as its own limitations and, at the same time, it will be in a position to offer its light – the light it gets from the soul – to the mind. We have to use the superior power, the light of the soul, to control the mind. If we try to control the mind before bringing down divine Light, we will sadly fail.

Meditating in the heart

The heart is like a fountain of peace, joy and love. You can sit at the base of the fountain and just enjoy. There is no need to pray to the Supreme to give you this, that, or anything else, for you will get all the things that you want and infinitely more from this fountain. But you will get them in the way the Supreme wants to give them. If you can please the Supreme by staying always in the presence of this fountain you will see that your desires are fulfilled most luminously. They may be the same desires you have always had, but they will be touched on a very high level with luminosity. Before they are fulfilled, the Supreme will transform each desire into aspiration with His Light.

When God transforms your desires into aspiration, you will see that you have become that aspiration itself. You can have that aspiration only in the heart and the soul, and not in the mind. If you go beyond the mind, you can also have the same aspiration. But you will never have it if you stay in the mind. The mind is really a dense jungle for most of us. Only in the heart will we find the sea of Peace and Bliss, and from there Light radiates.

Even if you do not get immediate results when meditating at home, please do not be disheartened or discouraged. To pass our school examinations, we have to study for years. But meditation is the examination of our body, vital, mind, heart and soul. When we pass this examination we have learned everything, whereas for the school examination we need only a very limited knowledge. For this vast inner knowledge we have to study. Our study is our sincere prayer and meditation. Sincerity plays a great part. If we meditate with intense sincerity even for two minutes, that is better than sitting in so-called meditation for two hours and thinking of our children, our friends, our enemies, our jobs and what not.

In India there are village women who say, "We meditate for six or eight hours every day. But God is so unkind, He never listens to our prayers." But what do they really do? They start meditation, and then they begin thinking of their cow. The cow is grazing and they wonder if it is entering into somebody else's territory and if it will be beaten. Their minds are roaming in the world of imagination, and then they say, "I have meditated for so many hours." But how many times did they even think of God, let alone feel God's Presence in their heart? The whole time they were uttering God's Name, but they were thinking of their cow or of some other trivial thing. What kind of result can anyone expect from this kind of meditation?

If we can remain for five minutes without any thought in our minds, divine or undivine, good or bad, then we immediately get the reflection of our soul. The soul represents our divine perfection both in our outer and in our inner life. Through pure meditation without thought, we become able to reflect our inner divinity.

As you concentrate on anything – a picture, a candle, a flame, any material object – so also can you concentrate on the heart. You may close your eyes or look at a wall, but all the time you are thinking of the heart as a dear friend of yours. When this thinking becomes most intense, when it absorbs your entire attention, then you have gone beyond the ordinary way of thinking and entered into concentration. You cannot look physically at your spiritual heart, but you can

focus all your attention on it. Then gradually, the power of your concentration enters into the heart and takes you completely out of the realm of the mind.

Meditation is the only way
To successfully replenish
Our heart-resources.

Exercises

Concentration on a flower

Try to look at the entire flower for a few seconds. While you are concentrating on the entire flower, please feel that you are the flower and also that this flower is growing inside your heart, in the inmost recesses of your heart. You are the flower and, at the same time, you are growing inside your heart.

Then, gradually try to concentrate on one particular petal, any petal that you select. At this time feel that that petal is the seed form of your reality-existence. Again, in a few minutes' time, please concentrate on the entire flower. At that time feel that it is the universal reality. So right now concentrate on the flower itself and then a few minutes later on one petal. In this way you go back and forth.

And please do not allow any thought to enter into your mind. Try to make your mind absolutely calm, quiet, tranquil, and kindly keep your eyes half open.

Meditation on the heart

Kindly keep your eyes half open and imagine the vast sky. Either try to see or feel the vast sky right in front of you. In the beginning try to feel that the sky is in front of you; then later please try to feel that you are as vast as the sky, or that you are the vast sky itself.

Now kindly close your eyes and try to see and feel the sky inside your heart. That is to say, please feel that you are now the Universal Heart, which you truly are. You are now the Universal Heart, and inside you is the sky that you meditated upon and identified yourself with. Your heart is infinitely, infinitely vaster than the sky, so you can easily house the sky within yourself.

Breathing techniques

Question: What is prana?

Sri Chinmoy: Prana is a Sanskrit word which means breath, life-breath or life-energy. This life-energy is not something material or physical that can be seen by the scientists or doctors, but it is indispensable to life. The source of prana is the Supreme. Prana is as important in our life as Atman, which is the soul or Self. Life is breath embodied and breath manifested.

There are five kinds of prana. The first is prana proper, the life-energy inside us. Wherever there is life, there is prana. The second is apana. This is the energy used specifically in excretion and generation. The third is samana. Samana is located around the navel and is used for digestion and assimilation. The fourth is called vyana. This is located in the lotus of our spiritual heart. There are 101 subtle spiritual nerves around this lotus, and from each of these nerves there branch out 101 other nerves. Each of these, in turn, has 72,000 branches, and through all these nerves vyana moves. These numbers may sound fantastic, but many Seers and Yogis have actually counted them. At the age of 22 or 23, I wanted to count these nerves, and I tried. I counted quite a few thousand, and then a luminous being stood in front of me and said, "Don't waste your time. The Seers are right."

The last form of prana is udana. Udana is located in the middle of the spine. This prana is most important. If this udana from the middle of the spine goes upward at the time of death, one will go to one of the higher worlds. If it goes downward, one will go to one of the lower worlds. Each place on the body represents a loka, a heavenly world. In India, at the time of death, the relatives and friends always try to observe the area from which the last life-breath of the deceased passes. If the last breath passes from anywhere below the navel, one has to go to lower worlds and suffer greatly. If it passes from somewhere above the navel, one will go to one of the higher worlds to enjoy the Delight of the Supreme.

Question: Could you speak a little about the secret of yogic breathing?

Sri Chinmoy: We have three major Yogas according to our Hindu spiritual philosophy: Jnana Yoga, Karma Yoga and Bhakti Yoga; the path of knowledge, the path of action and the path of devotion. In Jnana Yoga, the path of knowledge, there is a branch that is called Raja Yoga. Raja means 'king'. This branch is called the royal Yoga. In Raja Yoga there are eight steps or stages in the seeker's Godward journey, and the fourth is called pranayama. It is the Yoga of systematic breathing, of controlled breath. We all breathe, but most of us do not know how to breathe properly. Yet if we can breathe correctly, we can free ourselves from disease and ultimately we can even defy death.

There are two kinds of breath: one is prana and the other is apana. When we breathe in cosmic energy to purify and energise our life, we call it prana. When we breathe out our impurities, it is called apana. When we breathe in prana, we conquer disease, and when we breathe out apana, we put in perfect condition the physical organs that are not functioning well; that is to say, we put the entire body in perfect order.

Exercise

Here is a simple exercise that you can do at any time. While you are walking, for five steps breathe in and for five steps breathe out very regularly. If you do this for only two blocks, you will feel refreshed.

There are three steps in proper, systematic breathing. The first is puraka, or inhalation; the second is kumbhaka, or retention; the third is rechaka, or exhalation. When you breathe in, you have to feel that you are breathing in the Breath of God, the Supreme, the divine Beloved. When you hold the breath, you must feel that you are holding the all-fulfilling Breath of the Supreme. And when you breathe out, you have to feel that you are offering God's immortal Life-breath or energy to His entire creation.

In normal breathing both of your nostrils are usually functioning. But when you breathe properly through alternate nostrils, you get immediate relief from mental anxiety, worries, depression and many other things that cause disturbances in your nature.

Most of you have heard about Kundalini. This is the most sacred Yoga. Inside our spine in our subtle physical body, we have three currents.

They are called Ida, Pingala and Sushumna. Pingala has a connection with the sun, Ida with the moon, and Sushumna with the Highest. We have six spiritual centres in the spine, connected by these three currents. If we can open these centres we can become the possessors of infinite Peace, Light and Power. One other centre, which we call Sahasrara, the thousand-petaled lotus, is located in the cerebrum and is not counted with the other six. The other centres are Muladhara at the base of the spine, Svadisthana at the spleen, Manipura at the navel, Anahata at the heart, Vishuddha at the throat and Ajna in the forehead. We can open these centres with the power of our concentration, or with spiritual alternate breathing.

Question: I have been given to understand that in normal breathing we breathe in through both nostrils and then the energy goes down one side of the spine for two hours and then it goes down the other side for two hours; but that when we do alternate breathing, this changes. Is it true?

Sri Chinmoy: No, it is not true. The only thing that happens during normal breathing, when both nostrils are functioning, is that life energy goes up and down the spine. Spiritual figures are conscious of this; ordinary people are not. Prana goes upward to give realisation and downward for transformation. When prana goes up and passes through the Sahasrara chakra, it touches the Highest, like a link between Heaven and earth. When it goes down, it helps us keep a firm hold on matter, on the physical world. What actually happens during alternate breathing is that you put concentrated energy into your breathing in order to purify and divinely activate your system.

Twelve to fifteen breaths per minute is normal for most human beings, but there are people who breathe only three or four times a minute as a result of their practice of alternate breathing. The turtle is the symbol of Immortality. It breathes about three times per minute. That is why a turtle lives for hundreds of years while we live for only fifty, sixty or seventy years.

This technique of breathing gives success in all walks of life. It immediately takes us to the inner world and identifies us with the essence of our existence. From the soul we are reaching the Source, and when we are in the Source all is success and fulfilment.

For anything that you want to do, you will do better if you can hold your breath comfortably for a longer period. I happened to be a good sportsman in the hundred metre race. It is said that if you want to run a distance of a hundred metres, you should breathe in once and then cover the entire distance without breathing again. If you breathe in three or four times while you are running, you will be lost. Sometimes I could not do it in one breath and I had to take a second breath. Although I held the first prize for twelve years, I know I would have done far better if I could have done it always in one breath. Anything that you want to do, you will do better if you breathe in properly and hold your breath. But this should be done comfortably, without straining the lungs. While we are breathing ordinarily during the day, not even three or four times do we utilise our lungs so that they work to their full capacity. But proper breathing is very important. You know we are living in a world of economy. We always try to economise. If we can learn alternate breathing, then we are economising. And we get immediate success if we can do alternate breathing.

We must realize
That our inner strength
Is infinitely stronger
Than our outer incidents.

Breathing Exercises:

Cosmic energy

Feel that you are breathing in not air but cosmic energy. Feel that tremendous cosmic energy is entering into you with each breath and that you are going to use it to purify your body, vital, mind and heart. Feel that there is not a single place in your body that is not being occupied by the flow of cosmic energy. It is flowing like a river inside you, washing and purifying your whole being.

Then, when you start to breathe out, feel that you are breathing out all the rubbish inside you – all your undivine thoughts, obscure ideas and impure actions. Anything inside your system that you call undivine, anything that you do not want to claim as your own, feel that you are exhaling.

Breathe in peace, breathe out restlessness

Each time you breathe in, try to feel that you are bringing into your body peace, infinite peace. The opposite of peace is restlessness. When you breathe out, try to feel that you are expelling the restlessness within you and also the restlessness that you see all around you. When you breathe this way, you will find restlessness leaving you.

Breathe in power, breathe in joy

Please try to feel that you are breathing in power from the universe. And when you exhale, feel that all your fear is coming out of your body. After doing this a few times, try to feel that what you are breathing in is joy, infinite joy, and what you are breathing out is sorrow, suffering and melancholy.

Thread in front of the nose

Proper breathing is very important in meditation. When breathing, try to breathe in as slowly and quietly as possible, so that if somebody placed a tiny thread in front of your nose it would not move at all. And when you breathe out, try to breathe out even more slowly than when you breathed in. If possible, leave a short pause between the end of your first exhalation and the beginning of your second inhalation. If you can, hold your breath for a few seconds. But if it is difficult, do not do it. Never do anything that will harm your organs or respiratory system.

Breathe through different parts of your body

When you feel that you are tired, exhausted, please breathe in quietly. Take several deep breaths and try to feel that you are breathing in from various places. Try to feel that you are breathing in through the eyes, the ears, the forehead, through the crown of the head, through the shoulders and so on. When you are breathing in, if you are conscious of your breath, then you will not feel sleepy. But being conscious of your breath does not mean that you will make a sound. You will just feel that a stream of energy is entering into you with every breath. Feel that every place you are breathing in is a door. Each time you breathe in, you open a door here, there or somewhere else. Naturally, when you open the door, light enters. Then energy enters through the various doors into your body. This exercise is for everybody.

Breathe in purity

The first thing that you have to think of when breathing is purity. When you breathe in, it you can feel that the breath is coming directly from God, from Purity itself, then your breath can easily be purified.

222

Your breath is God's playground

Try to feel that your heart is a vast playground, and that inside this playground there is a special and sacred place where God likes to play. That chosen place is inside your life-breath. Each time you breathe in or breathe out, try to feel that the breath you are inhaling or exhaling is for God. When you are breathing in good thoughts, you have to feel that those good thoughts are for God. And when you are breathing out undivine thoughts, you have to feel that those undivine thoughts are also for God. You don't have to count how many good thoughts you have breathed in or how many bad thoughts you have breathed out. No! Only you have to remember that, good or bad, each breath of yours is for God only.

*The Source of power is infinitely greater
Than the physical strength
That any human being can have.*

Explanatory Notes

AUM

Aum is a syllable with a special significance and creative power. Aum is the mother of all mantras. When we chant AUM, what actually happens is that we bring down Peace and Light from above and create a universal harmony within and without us. When we repeat AUM, both our inner and our outer beings become inspired and surcharged with divine Light and aspiration. AUM has no equal. AUM has infinite Power. Just by repeating AUM, we can realise God.

Aspiration

Aspiration is our soul's mounting cry to reach the Highest and to bring down the Highest into the earth's consciousness.

Chakras

There are three principal channels through which this life–energy flows. These channels meet together at six different places. Each meeting place forms a centre. Each centre is round like a wheel. Indian spiritual philosophy calls these centres chakras. All real spiritual Masters, from the very depth of their experience, say that it is better to open the heart centre first and then try to open the other centres.

The Crown Centre

There are seven major psychic centres in our body. These centres are not in the physical, but in the subtle body. At the crown of the head is one called Sahasrara, the thousand–petalled lotus. Sahasrara is the highest, the most peaceful, the most soulful, the most fruitful of all the centres. When one enters into this crown centre, he enters into trance and goes beyond the consciousness of this world.

God-Realisation

God–Realisation is nothing short of a spiritual science which puts an end to suffering, ignorance and death. But we have to realise God for His sake and not for our sake. To seek God for one's own sake is to feed one's ceaseless desires in vain. But to seek God for His sake is to live in His Universal Consciousness; in other words, to be one with Him absolutely and inseparably.

Guru

A real spiritual Master is one who has attained God-realisation. Everyone is one with God, but the real spiritual Master has established his conscious oneness with God. At any moment he can enter into a higher consciousness and bring down messages from God to those disciples who have faith in him. The Master, if he is genuine, represents God on earth for those seekers who have real aspiration and faith in him. He has been authorised or commissioned by God to help them.

The real Teacher, the real Guru, is God Himself. But on earth He will often operate in and through a spiritual Master. The Master energises the seeker with inspiration and, in the course of time, through the infinite Grace of the Supreme, offers the seeker illumination.

The Guru is not the body. The Guru is the revelation and manifestation of a divine Power upon earth.

The Navel Centre

The navel chakra or Manipura, is the third chakra. This chakra should not be opened up until the heart centre is opened up. If the navel centre is opened before the heart, then the lowest vital, the most impure vital, may enter into the heart and destroy all your spiritual possibilities. The navel centre is also the emotional centre (see also Vital).

The Spiritual Heart

The spiritual heart is located right in the centre of the chest. If you find it difficult to meditate on the spiritual heart, you can concentrate on the physical heart in the chest. But after you meditate there for a few months or for a year, you will feel that inside the ordinary human heart is the divine heart, and inside the divine heart is the soul. When you feel this, you will start meditating on the spiritual heart.

Supreme

There is one God called by many different names. I like the term 'Supreme'. All religious faiths have the same God but they address Him differently. A man will be called 'Father' by one person, 'Brother' by another and 'Uncle' by another. Similarly, God is also addressed in various ways, according to one's sweetest, most affectionate feeling. Instead of using the word 'God', I use the word 'Supreme' most of the time. When we say 'Supreme', we are speaking of the Supreme Lord who not only reaches the absolute Highest, but all the time goes beyond, beyond and transcends the Beyond.

The Third Eye

Third Eye, also called Ajna chakra, is located between and a little above the eyebrows. It is the most powerful centre. He who has mastery over the Ajna chakra destroys his dark past, hastens the golden future and manifests the present in a supremely fulfilling way.

The Vital

Each human being is composed of five elements: body, vital, mind, heart and soul. There are two vitals in us: one is the dynamic vital and the other is the aggressive vital. The vital embodies either divine dynamism or hostile aggression. When the aspirant brings the soul's light to the fore, the hostile aggression changes into the divine dynamism and the divine dynamism is transformed into the all-fulfilling supreme Reality.

Emotion and the vital are two different things. You can say that the vital is the house and in that house emotion is the tenant. The most predominant emotion is the vital emotion. But emotion can also be in the body, in the mind and in the heart.

Yoga

Yoga means union, conscious union with God. We are one with the Self, but we are not now aware of it. We can become aware of it only when we consciously practise spirituality; and for that we need aspiration. When we are marching along the path of aspiration, our soul will automatically blend with our physical being and the physical being will devotedly listen to the dictates of the soul. Then we will see that our inner life and our outer life have become totally one.

Yoga is neither a philosophy nor a religion. Yoga transcends both philosophy and religion; at the same time, it houses both religion and philosophy. Religion and philosophy can lead a human being up to God's palace, while Yoga means union with God, man's conscious union with God.

Sri Ramakrishna (1836–1886)

Sri Ramakrishna was a great Indian spiritual master whose life was a testament to truth, universality, love and purity. When he as a young man became a temple priest, he was seized by an unquenchable thirst for union with God, and he immersed himself in intense meditation and other spiritual practices.

Ramakrishna was constantly absorbed in the thought of God. He would often go into high spiritual states where he would merge with the Infinite Reality. For him, the Vedantic teaching of unity of all existence was more than theory; he literally saw, and knew, this to be true.

In his thirst for the divine, Ramakrishna followed different religious paths including various branches of Hinduism. Not content to stop there, however, he also practised Islam and later meditated deeply on the Christ, experiencing the same divine Reality through these non-Hindu paths. Thus, he came to the conclusion, based on his direct experience, that all religions lead to the same goal.

Swami Vivekananda (1863–1902)

Swami Vivekananda was the most notable disciple of Sri Ramakrishna, who demonstrated the essential unity of all religions. Vivekananda's inspiring personality was well known both in India and in America during the last decade of the nineteenth century and the first decade of the twentieth. The unknown monk of India suddenly leapt into fame at the Parliament of Religions held in Chicago in 1893, at which he represented Hinduism. His vast knowledge of Eastern and Western culture as well as his deep spiritual insight, fervid eloquence, brilliant conversation, broad human sympathy, and colourful personality made an irresistible appeal to the many types of Westerners who came in contact with him.

Rabindranath Tagore (1861–1941)

Rabindranath Tagore was a Bengali poet, composer, novelist and painter best known for being the first non–European to be awarded the Nobel Prize for Literature in 1913 with his book Gitanjali, Song Offerings. He was highly influential in introducing Indian culture to the West and is generally regarded as the outstanding creative artist of modern India.

Pandava family

In the Mahabharata, a Hindu epic text, the Pandavas are the five acknowledged sons of Pandu, by his two wives Kunti and Madri. Their names are Yudhishthira, Bhima, Arjuna, Nakula and Sahadeva. All five brothers were married to the same woman, Draupadi. Together the brothers fought and prevailed in a great war against their cousins the Kauravas, which came to be known as the Battle of Kurukshetra.

A conversation between Arjuna and his teacher and friend Krishna on the battlefield of Kurukshetra was immortalised in the Bhagavad Gita, one of the most compelling and important texts of the Hindu tradition.

About the author

Sri Chinmoy was born in the village of Shakpura in East Bengal, India (now Bangladesh) in 1931. He was the youngest of seven children in a devout family. In 1944, after the passing of both of his parents, he joined his brothers and sisters at the Sri Aurobindo Ashram, a spiritual community near Pondicherry in South India. He meditated for several hours a day, having many deep inner experiences. It was here that he first began writing poetry to convey his widening mystical vision. He also took an active part in Ashram life and was a champion athlete for many years.

Heeding an inner command, Sri Chinmoy moved to the United States in 1964 to be of service to spiritual aspirants in the Western world. During the 43 years that he lived in the West he opened more than 100 meditation Centres worldwide and served as spiritual guide to thousands of students. Sri Chinmoy's boundless creativity found expression not only in poetry and other forms of literature, but also in musical composition and performance, art and sport. In each sphere he sought to convey the diverse experiences that comprise the spiritual journey: the search for truth and beauty, the struggle to transcend limitations, and the supremely fulfilling communion of the human soul with the Divine.

As a self-described student of peace who combined Eastern spirituality and Western dynamism in a remarkable way, Sri Chinmoy garnered international renown. In 1970 at the request of U Thant, the third Secretary-General of the United Nations, he began the twice-weekly peace meditations for delegates and staff members at UN headquarters that continued until the end of his life. Sri Chinmoy enjoyed a special friendship with many international luminaries including

President Mikhail Gorbachev, Mother Teresa, President Nelson Mandela and Archbishop Desmond Tutu.

On 11 October 2007, Sri Chinmoy passed beyond the curtain of Eternity. His creative, peace-loving and humanitarian endeavours are carried on worldwide by his students, who practise meditation and strive to serve the world in accordance with his timeless teachings.

For more information about Sri Chinmoy kindly visit

www.**srichinmoy**.org

Recommended books by Sri Chinmoy

The Adventure of Life

On Yoga, Meditation, and the Art of Living

A modern-day spiritual manual that encourages
the reader to embrace new ideas, adding
a deeper, spiritual dimension to one's life.
In a clear and accessible way, Sri Chinmoy speaks
about the spiritual art of living, society and
religion as well as popular topics such as chakras,
occult powers and the end of the world, and
introduces us to a modern spiritual lifestyle with
focus on health, diet, sport, family life and the workplace.

(www.**lifeadventure**.net)

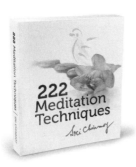

222 Meditation Techniques

These 222 guided exercises, the largest
collection of meditation techniques in one
book, are suitable for both beginners and
advanced seekers who wish to explore
the world of meditation. From breathing
exercises, guided meditations and the use
of mantras, to special exercises for runners,
artists and musicians, ways to overcome
depression, stress and bad habits, and even losing weight, this book
offers a truly broad canvas of possibilities.

(www.**themeditationbook**.net)

Sport & Meditation

The Inner Dimension of Sport

This is a unique book, which challenges our preconceptions of our physical capacities and of the limitations of age. It includes specific exercises concerning meditation, concentration and mantra as aids to the focus needed in all forms of exercise and training. It is this new facet that enables us to achieve peak performance, to get more from exercise and to enjoy robust and lasting health and wellbeing.

World champions such as Carl Lewis, Tatyana Lebedeva, Tegla Loroupe, Bill Pearl, and Paul Tergat share their own inner secrets and spiritual perspectives on training and competition in anecdotes peppered throughout the book.

(www.**sportandmeditation**.com)

Angels and Fairies

In this beautifully illustrated book Sri Chinmoy offers profound insight into the connection between angels and fairies and the role that these beings play in relation to us, with the confidence of someone who has attained free access to the inner realms.

(www.**bluebeyondbooks**.co.uk)